MW00635904

CLEAN SIMPLE EATS

WELCOME TO THE CSE SQUAD!

Hi! We're JJ and Erika, the husband and wife behind Clean Simple Eats! We are passionate about helping others elevate their lives through food and fitness, and we are here to prove that clean eating can be simple, fun and satisfying. That's why we've put a healthy spin on delicious comfort food recipes we all know and love (hello Turkey Pot Pie and Pumpkin French Toast).

Frustrated by bland and boring diets, we started experimenting with recipes, substituting more healthful ingredients and before we knew it, Clean Simple Eats was born! But we couldn't stop there; we created four seasonal 7-week macro-balanced Meal Plans filled with hundreds of delicious, family-friendly recipes with just the right amount of protein, fat and carbs to keep your body fueled and satisfied. Our Meal Plans have proven to please even the pickiest of eaters (aka our four kiddos), and we guarantee that these meals will teach lifelong healthy habits.

Aside from our recipes, we've also created our own line of clean and tasty protein powders, supplements, and mixed nut butters (aka Off-Beat Butters, so yummy you'll want to eat them #bythespoonful). Our goal was (and is still) to create the best-tasting, highest quality products on the market, and we believe we did just that! Each small-batch flavor combo is unique, crave-worthy, and sure to leave you asking for more!

We believe that healthy habits + consistency over time yield the very best results, which means a sustainable diet is key. We also believe in the importance of a community that supports you. Here at CSE, we have a strong community called the CSE Squad! Our #CSESquad are strong and loyal rock stars who are willing to embrace a challenge—the #CSEChallenge.

It's been a great adventure, but the very best part is watching others take control of their narrative, reach goals, find inner confidence and transform their lives. That is the reason why we do what we do! We can't wait to be a part of your health and fitness journey!

Eat **clean,** keep it **simple,** get **results**.

In this plan you'll find:

• 7 weeks of macro-friendly recipes that your whole family will love
• Menu planners and shopping lists for each week
• Weekly meal prep suggestions
• A Fast Food Macro Guide
• A Food Swaps List
• Calorie and macronutrient breakdowns for each individual recipe
• Calorie Quick List: determine how many meals/snacks you need
• Intro to Macros: how to customize this plan to fit your goals
• 11 workouts programmed by certified personal trainer, JJ Peterson

STAY
CONNECTED

📷 cleansimpleeats / cleansimplefit

📘 facebook.com/groups/cleansimpleeats

✉ hello@cleansimpleeats.com

▶ www.cleansimpleeats.com

HOW TO USE THIS PLAN

• We designed this plan to make your weekly menu planning, grocery shopping and meal prep simple! Each grocery list includes enough groceries for breakfast, lunch and dinner for two adults each week. Make sure to add the ingredients for the snacks you choose each week to your shopping list! Snacks are not included on the grocery lists. You'll notice a menu pattern in this meal plan. Simple breakfasts on the weekdays, fun breakfasts on the weekends. Fresh, new dinners each night making enough to enjoy that dinner again for lunch the following day. Simple meal prep! Lunch is always ready to go! We built in two meals a week for dining out using our Fast Food Macros Guide.

• We encourage you to start at the beginning of the plan. Even if you're jumping into the challenge at a later date, start with Week 1. The groceries on each weekly grocery list will give you all the ingredients needed for meals that week through to Monday's lunch of the following week.

• The majority of the entrees in this meal plan make four servings. Breakfasts make anywhere from one to four servings. This meal plan was created to feed two adults. If you are feeding a family, you will want to double or triple each recipe to give you enough servings to feed each person. If you're using this plan by yourself, you can either cut each recipe and grocery list in half or keep the portions where they're at and cook fewer meals each week. Before making adjustments, make sure to check how many servings each meal makes and how many caloires you need per day to reach your goal.

• One note about the "dine out" meals. We wouldn't recommend eating more than your maintenance calories for the day, especially if your goal is weight loss. For example, if your maintenance calories equal 2,000, you would want to stick to 2,000 calories or less for the day (including your dine out meal) to keep you on track to reaching your goals. You wouldn't want to ruin all the progress you've made for the week all in one meal! It can happen fast! Refer to the "Tips for Dining Out"page and our "Fast Food Macros Guide" included in this book to help you stay mindful when dining out.

• If there are meals you don't prefer, remember that all meals are interchangeable. You can swap out any meal you'd like for another. You can always visit our website, cleansimpleeats.com/resources to download your own blank menu planner and grocery list. Our CSE+ App also makes menu planning super easy!

• Make sure to familiarize yourself with the Food Prep Guide at the beginning of this book. There are weekly meal prep recommendations found in this section that, if followed, will save you a ton of time and help to keep you on point during the challenge.

• The HIIT workouts that you'll find toward the back of the book are completely optional, but we know you'll love them! These workouts were programmed by JJ (who is a certified personal trainer) and have been designed to burn fat and build muscle. Plan to repeat the Monday workout for 7 Mondays in a row, the Tuesday workout for 7 Tuesdays, etc. Track your progress and improvements each week.

LET'S GET STARTED!

1. Grab a buddy to start this plan with you. Having an accountability partner will double your chances of success!

2. Before you shop, read over the provided weekly shopping list and cross out any items that you might already have on hand (we suggest you do this every week before shopping). Clean out your pantry and fridge. Throw away any junk food or trigger foods that might derail your progress during the next 7 weeks.

3. Drink lots of water. We suggest that you drink half of your bodyweight in ounces of water every day. Even more if you are active!

4. Take before pictures and measurements. Pictures and measurements are the best way to show how far you have come.

WE BELIEVE IN YOU! YOU'VE GOT THIS!

A BIT ABOUT MACROS

This is a "macro-based" meal plan, meaning every recipe has a balanced macronutrient ratio of 40% carbs, 30% protein and 30% fat. This 40/30/30 approach has been proven time and time again to offer balance and lifelong sustainability. The most beautiful part about the CSE meal plans (minus the food itself) is the fact that you can eat like this forever! This meal plan was designed to help you AND your family gain lasting healthy habits in the kitchen and a positive relationship with food. Don't worry too much about the science behind this meal plan. We've done all the hard work for you!

What are macros and why do they need to be balanced? Macronutrients are nutrients that provide calories or energy. Nutrients are substances needed for growth, metabolism, and for other body functions. Since "macro" means large, macronutrients are nutrients needed in large amounts.

There are three macronutrients:

• **Protein**
• **Fat**
• **Carbohydrates**

While each of these macros provide calories, the amount of calories that each one provides varies.

Carbohydrates: 4 calories per gram
Protein: 4 calories per gram
Fat: 9 calories per gram

This means that if you looked at the Nutrition Facts label of a product and it said 12 grams of carbs, 0 grams of fat, and 0 grams of protein per serving, you would know that this food has about 48 calories per serving (12 grams carbs multiplied by 4 calories for each gram of carbohydrate = 48 calories).

WHY DO WE NEED CARBOHYDRATES?
• The body's preferred source of fuel and energy
• Can be easily used by the body for energy
• All of the tissues and cells in our body can use glucose for energy
• Needed for the central nervous system, the kidneys, the brain, and the muscles (including the heart) to function properly.
• Can be stored in the muscles and liver for later use of energy
• Important in intestinal health and waste elimination

Carbohydrates are mainly found in starchy foods (like grains and potatoes), fruits, milk, and yogurt. Other foods like vegetables, beans, nuts, seeds, and cottage cheese contain carbohydrates, but in lesser amounts.

WHY DO WE NEED PROTEIN?
• Tissue repair
• Immune function
• Making essential hormones and enzymes
• Building and preserving lean muscle mass
• Growth (especially for children, teens, and pregnant women)

Protein is found in meats, poultry, fish, tofu, cheese, milk, nuts, legumes, and in smaller quantities in starchy foods and vegetables.

WHY DO WE NEED FAT?
• Normal growth, development and cell function
• Energy (fat is the most concentrated source of energy)
• Absorbing certain vitamins (like vitamins A, D, E, K, and carotenoids)
• Maintaining cell membranes for healthy skin and other tissues
• Needed for proper functioning of nerves and brain
• Regulate hormones and many bodily processes
• Providing taste, consistency, and stability to foods

Fat is found in meat, poultry, nuts, milk products, butters, oils, fish, grain products and salad dressings. There are three main types of fat: trans fat, saturated fat, and unsaturated fat. Completely eliminate trans fats from your diet if possible. These fats are found in fried foods, processed foods, fast foods, and snack foods. Limit the saturated fats coming from animal products and go with coconut oil! Stick to good, healthy fats that you find in avocados, avocado oil, EVOO, nuts, and nut butters.

CUSTOMIZE YOUR PLAN

DOWNLOAD THE CSE+ APP

Available in the App Store or Google Play. Input your personal information to customize your goals and you're all set! For more information, visit cleansimpleeats.com/pages/app

MACRO QUICK LIST

CHOOSE ONE OF THE TWO OPTIONS LISTED BELOW YOUR CUSTOM
CALORIE COUNT TO REACH YOUR DAILY MACRO GOAL

 1250 - 1300 CALORIES: 42F / 125C / 94P
3 MEAL SERVINGS + 1 SNACK SERVING
3 MEAL SERVINGS + 2 POWER BITES

 1500 - 1550 CALORIES: 50F / 150C / 113P
3 MEAL SERVINGS + 2 SNACK SERVINGS
3 MEAL SERVINGS + 1 SNACK SERVING + 2 POWER BITES

 1750 - 1800 CALORIES: 58F / 175C / 131P
3 MEAL SERVINGS + 3 SNACK SERVINGS
3 MEAL SERVINGS + 2 SNACK SERVINGS + 2 POWER BITES

 2000 - 2050 CALORIES: 67F / 200C / 150P
3 MEAL SERVINGS + 3 SNACK SERVINGS + 2 POWER BITES
4 MEAL SERVINGS + 2 SNACK SERVINGS + 1 POWER BITE

 2250 - 2300 CALORIES: 75F / 225C / 169P
4 MEAL SERVINGS + 3 SNACK SERVINGS + 1 POWER BITE
3 MEAL SERVINGS + 4 SNACK SERVINGS + 2 POWER BITES

 2500 - 2550 CALORIES: 83F / 250C / 188P
5 MEAL SERVINGS + 2 SNACK SERVINGS + 2 POWER BITES
6 MEAL SERVINGS + 1 SNACK SERVING + 1 POWER BITE

 2750 - 2800 CALORIES: 92F / 275C / 206P
6 MEAL SERVINGS + 2 SNACK SERVINGS + 2 POWER BITES
6 MEAL SERVINGS + 3 SNACK SERVINGS

 3000 - 3050 CALORIES: 100F / 300C / 225P
6 MEAL SERVINGS + 4 SNACK SERVINGS
6 MEAL SERVINGS + 3 SNACK SERVINGS + 2 POWER BITES

The ideas, concepts and opinions expressed in all Clean Simple Eats meal plans, books and other media are intended to be used for educational purposes only. The books and meal plans are sold with the understanding that authors and publisher are not rendering medical advice of any kind, nor are the books or meal plans intended to replace medical advice, nor to diagnose, prescribe or treat any disease, condition, illness or injury. By my use of any of the products and/or programs of Clean Simple Eats, I am agreeing to assume all of the risks associated with such use. I further agree to waive, release, and discharge Clean Simple Eats from any and all liability arising from its negligence or fault.

It is imperative that before beginning any diet or exercise program, including any aspect of the Clean Simple Eats program, you receive full medical clearance from a licensed physician.

Authors and publisher claim no responsibility to any person or entity for any liability, loss or damage caused or alleged to be caused directly or indirectly as a result of the use, application or interpretation of the material in the books or meal plan.

The Food and Drug Administration has not evaluated the statements contained in any Clean Simple Eats books, meal plans, or other media.

This book, and any other Clean Simple Eats seasonal meal plan or book, is protected under copyright laws and may not be duplicated, shared, copied or plagiarized, under any circumstance, in digital or bound form.

©2022 CLEAN SIMPLE EATS, INC
ITEM NOT FOR RESALE OR DISTRIBUTION

RECIPE

INDEX

SNACKS
Apple Crisp Smoothie ... 51
Apple Crumb Muffin & Vanilla Shake ... 95
Apple Slaw & Crackers ... 75
Apples, Nuts, Jerky & Greens Detox Drink ... 73
Broccoli, Cheddar & Bacon Omelet ... 85
Chocolate Covered Strawberry Parfait ... 61
Chocolate Fondue Power Dip ... 91
Cookie Crumb Granola ... 67
Cookie Crumb Granola Parfait ... 65
Greek Escape ... 69
Kiwi & Pomegranate Parfait ... 63
Milk & Cookies ... 55
Mini Quiche Muffins ... 83
Open-Faced Turkey & Veggie Sandwich ... 71
Over-Easy Eggs & Hash ... 81
PB Pumpkin Cream Shake ... 45
PB Toast & Eggs ... 79
Peanut Butter Cookie Shake ... 49
Post-Workout Strawberry Milk ... 53
Post-Workout Strawberry Milkshake ... 53
Pumpkin Chocolate Chip Mug Muffin ... 87
Pumpkin Cream Pancakes ... 93
Pumpkin Pie Parfait ... 57
Pumpkin Spice Shake ... 47
Spiced Banana Almond Shake ... 43
Spiced White Hot Chocolate ... 89
Sweet Pear Parfait ... 59
Turkey Muffins ... 77

POWER BITES
Almond Coconut Brownie Bites ... 103
Caramel Macchiato Bites ... 99
Coconut Cashew Macaroon Bites ... 107
Fall Cookie Dough Bites ... 97
Pumpkin Pie Energy Bites ... 105
Snickers Power Bites ... 101
Toasted Coconut Cashew Butter ... 107

BREAKFASTS
Almond Joy Protein Shake ... 111
Apple Butter Crepes ... 129
Apple Cinnamon Protein Pancakes ... 113
Bacon, Egg & Avocado Sandwich ... 125
Breakfast Burritos ... 117
Cinna-Berry Breakfast Squares ... 135
Double Chocolate PB Oatmeal ... 127
Hot Apple Pie Oats ... 119
Lemon Raspberry Flourless Crepes ... 137
One Pan Country Skillet ... 133
Pumpkin French Toast ... 131
Pumpkin Pie Overnight Oats ... 115
Pumpkin Protein Waffles ... 121
Superfood Cereal ... 123

ENTREES
Autumn Salad Sandwich ... 141
BBQ Beef Sandwich & Slaw ... 153
BBQ Chicken Avocado Wrap ... 193
Beef & Broccoli Stir-Fry ... 171
BLTA Waffle Sandwich ... 215
Buffalo Chicken & Mozz Meatballs ... 223
Butternut Squash & Sausage Risotto ... 191
Caprese Pasta Bowl ... 195
Cheddar Ranch Chicken & Potatoes ... 201
Cheesy Roasted Veggies & Sausage ... 211
Chicken Enchilada Stuffed Squash ... 143
Chicken Fettuccine Alfredo ... 155
Chinese Sesame Chicken ... 225
Cranberry, Pear & Turkey Salad ... 173
Creamy Chicken Corn Chowder ... 187
Fall Maple Hash ... 205
Garden Veggie Pizza ... 175
Grilled Caprese Panini ... 179
Grilled Cheese & Tomato Basil Soup ... 161
Harvest Cobb Salad ... 147
Honey-Garlic Chicken Tacos ... 157
Maple Dijon Protein Bowl ... 199
Maple Pecan Glazed Salmon ... 185
Mediterranean Bounty Bowl ... 209
Open-Faced Tuna Melt ... 159
Parmesan Crusted Salmon ... 149
Pepperoni Pizza Pinwheels ... 151
Pesto Chicken Sliders ... 219
Philly Cheesesteak Wraps ... 221
Roasted Butternut Squash Soup ... 183
Salsa Chicken Pile-Up ... 181
Salsa Verde Chicken Burritos ... 169
Shepherd's Pie ... 189
Sloppy Sweet Potato ... 207
Stacked Chicken Enchiladas ... 217
Taco Soup ... 145
Thai Chicken Pizza ... 163
Thai Chicken Soup ... 197
Thai Peanut Spaghetti ... 167
Thai Protein Bowl ... 177
Tomato Basil Spaghetti & Meatballs ... 203
Turkey Pot Pies ... 165
White Chicken Chili ... 213

OTHER
Cashew Sour Cream ... 39

WORKOUTS ... 226

TIPS FOR
DINING OUT

If you know the restaurant you're going to be dining at ahead of time, look up the menu online to see if they have nutrition facts. Find something that will work in your calorie range. If they don't have nutrition information listed, just look the menu over and pick the item that looks the healthiest to you. Decide beforehand what you are going to order, so that when you get to the restaurant all those yummy smells don't sway your decision! Most restaurants have "healthy" or "skinny" menu options that will be fewer calories.

Salads are always a good choice! Watch out for candied nuts, lots of cheese, dressings and/or calorie packed toppings (chips or fried wontons). I would recommend omitting the dressing and asking for a couple of lemons. Squeeze that juice on your salad with a little salt and black pepper and you're good to go. Pack stevia packets or your own low-calorie dressing in your bag that you can use. That will help to add flavor to your salad as well. Make sure your salad includes a lean protein source, a small amount of healthy fat, and a lot of veggies.

Ordering basic individual meal components work great as well. Try to create a plate that you'd have at home: a protein source (size of your palm), a healthy fat source (size of your thumb), a complex carb (size of your fist), plus some veggies. Request that the chef prepare your food without the addition of any butter, oil or sauces.

Good luck and enjoy your night out!

Café Rio
• Grilled Chicken Salad, no tortilla, rice, lettuce, pico, cilantro, lime, bring 2 T. Bolthouse Farms Cilantro Avocado Dressing
352 calories | 15F | 33C | 22P
• Grilled Chicken Tostada on white corn tortilla, rice, lettuce, pico, cilantro, lime
408 calories | 14F | 37C | 37P
• Grilled Chicken Tacos (2) on white corn tortilla, rice, lettuce, pico, cilantro, lime
466 calories | 10F | 40C | 58P
• Grilled Salmon Tacos (2) on white corn tortillas, rice, lettuce, pico, cilantro, lime
352 calories | 10F | 36C | 34P
• Grilled Steak Tacos (2) on white corn tortillas, rice, lettuce, pico, cilantro, lime
378 calories | 12F | 34C | 36P
• Mahi Mahi Tacos (2) on white corn tortillas, rice, lettuce, pico, cilantro, lime
278 calories | 6F | 30C | 30P

Café Zupas
• Asian Citrus Chicken Salad – large, no dressing *270 calories | 13F | 19C | 20P*
• BBQ Chicken Salad – large, no dressing
310 calories | 10F | 34C | 18P
• Strawberry Harvest Chicken – large, no dressing *260 calories | 12F | 19C | 18P*
• Chocolate Covered Strawberry
45 calories | 2F | 7C | 1P

California Pizza Kitchen
• Sesame Dumplings
328 calories | 8F | 45C | 19P
• OG BBQ Chicken Pizza - 2 Slices
378 calories | 10F | 50C | 22P
• Cali Veggie Pizza - 2 Slices
386 calories | 10F | 50C | 24P
• Jamaican Jerk Pizza - 2 Slices
430 calories | 14F | 52C | 24P
• Wild Mushroom Pizza
+ Chicken - 2 Slices
397 calories | 13F | 46C | 24P

Cheesecake Factory
• Skinnylicious Mexican Chicken Lettuce Wraps
220 calories | 9F | 14C | 24P
• Skinnylicious Turkey Burger
336 calories | 8F | 38C | 28P

Chick-Fil-A
• Grilled Chicken Sandwich, no sauce
320 calories | 5F | 40C | 30P
• Asian Salad, no dressing
330 calories | 13F | 24C | 29P
• Grilled Chicken Cool Wrap
330 calories | 12F | 28C | 38P
• Chicken Tortilla Soup, medium
260 calories | 6F | 29C | 22P

Chipotle
• Chicken Salad: lettuce, chicken, ½ brown rice, ½ black beans, tomato salsa
360 calories | 10F | 30C | 38P

Corelife Eatery
• Big Spicy Chicken & Ancient Grains Bowl
290 calories | 8F | 29C | 26P
• Big Spicy Thai Chicken & Rice Noodles Bowl
310 calories | 4F | 47C | 23P
• Small Poke Bowl
350 calories | 22F | 21C | 28P
• Big Berry Quinoa Chicken Bowl
420 calories | 17F | 41C | 29P
• Small BBQ Ranch Chicken Bowl
430 calories | 10F | 56C | 29P
• Small Spicy Chicken Bowl
360 calories | 11F | 40C | 26P
• Big Chicken & Rice Noodle Broth Bowl
310 calories | 1.5F | 40C | 31P
• Small Chicken Tortilla & Chipotle Broth Bowl
300 calories | 5F | 30C | 31P
• Small Spicy Ginger & Steak Rice Noodle Broth Bowl
320 calories | 11F | 24C | 32P

Costa Vida

• Taco, one: Black beans, chicken or mahi mahi, lettuce, lime, pico de gallo w/corn tortilla: *320 calories | 6F | 44C | 23P*
w/whole wheat tortilla:
350 calories | 10F | 42C | 24P
• Raspberry Chicken Salad, Small: Whole wheat tortilla, chicken, black beans, lettuce, raspberry chipotle sauce, pico
380 calories | 10F | 51C | 23P
• Baja Bowl: Rice, chicken, tomatillo cilantro sauce, lettuce, pico de gallo
380 calories | 10F | 38C | 33P

Culver's

• Grilled Chicken Sandwich
387 calories | 7F | 40C | 41P
• Beef Pot Roast Sandwich
410 calories | 13F | 40C | 31P
• Grilled Chicken Caesar Salad
308 calories | 12F | 17C | 33P
• Garden Fresco & Grilled Chicken Salad
350 calories | 14F | 15C | 44P

The Habit Burger Grill

• Lettuce Wrap Charburger
352 calories | 19F | 3C | 18P
• Chargrilled Ahi Tuna Sandwich
390 calories | 10F | 51C | 28P
• Grilled Chicken Salad, no dressing
410 calories | 15F | 35C | 35P

Einstein Bros. Bagels

• Thintastic Turkey Sausage & Cheddar Egg White Sandwich
330 calories | 10F | 35C | 25P
• Thintastic Southwest Egg White Sandwich
330 calories | 10F | 35C | 24P
• Thintastic Santa Fe Egg White Sandwich
410 calories | 16F | 42C | 25P
• Thintastic Tasty Turkey Sandwich
431 calories | 15F | 45C | 29P
• Thintastic Buffalo Chicken Sandwich
430 calories | 12F | 50C | 32P

Fueled Fresh Kitchen

• Breakfast Hash
404 calories | 8F | 36C | 43P

• Breakfast Sandwich w/sausage
362 calories | 12F | 33C | 30P
• Greek Yogurt
360 calories | 7F | 49C | 29P
• Fueled Veggie Omelet
286 calories | 7F | 31C | 25P
• PB Vacation Shake
409 calories | 9F | 41C | 46P
• Chocolate PB Love Shake
419 calories | 9F | 44C | 46P
• Island Breeze Shake
400 calories | 12F | 47C | 32P
• Fueled Beast Shake
312 calories | 16F | 19C | 30P
• Yoda Shake
328 calories | 15F | 26C | 30P
• Very Berry Acai Smoothie
309 calories | 9F | 30C | 28P
• Tropical Paradise Acai Smoothie
363 calories | 13F | 35C | 28P
• Nuts N' Berries Acai Smoothie
436 calories | 15F | 32C | 45P
• Blackened BBQ Chicken Bowl
*without carb option
321 calories | 4F | 29C | 43P
• Chicken Curry Bowl
*without carb option
325 calories | 9F | 17C | 44P
• Skinny Salmon Bowl
386 calories | 19F | 17C | 39P
• Teriyaki Bowl
*without carb option
312 calories | 5F | 22C | 43P
• Poke Tacos
376 calories | 12F | 43C | 28P
• Bruschetta Steak Tacos
371 calories | 14F | 38C | 27P

In-N-Out

• Double Hamburger protein style, add mustard instead of spread
340 calories | 23F | 11C | 33P
• Hamburger w/mustard & ketchup instead of spread
310 calories | 10F | 41C | 16P

Jack's
• Grilled Chicken Salad
310 calories | 13F | 18C | 34P
• Grilled Chicken Sandwich
410 calories | 17F | 35C | 29P

Kneaders
• ½ Turkey, Bacon, Avocado Sandwich
370 calories | 15F | 42C | 21P
• Turkey Cranberry Sunflower Salad, no dressing
340 calories | 15F | 26C | 26P
• White Bean Chicken Chili
190 calories | 3F | 19C | 21P

McDonald's
• Egg White Delight McMuffin
250 calories | 7F | 30C | 18P
• Fruit & Maple Oatmeal, no brown sugar, add ½ serving CSE Protein Powder
320 calories | 4F | 51C | 17P
• Southwest Salad w/ grilled chicken, no dressing
290 calories | 8F | 28C | 27P
• Bacon Ranch Salad with Grilled Chicken, no dressing
230 calories | 9F | 10C | 30P
• Honey Mustard Snack Wrap, Grilled or Chipotle BBQ Snack Wrap, Grilled
250 calories | 8F | 27C | 16P
• Grilled Chicken Sandwich, no sauce
350 calories | 9F | 42C | 28P
• McWrap Sweet Chili Chicken
360 calories | 9F | 43C | 26P

MOD Pizza
• Mini Jasper
340 calories | 11F | 41C | 18P
• Mini Dillon James, add chicken
410 calories | 12.5F | 51C | 21.5P
• Mini Caspian
420 calories | 13F | 54C | 22P
• Mini Chicken, Mushroom & Tomato
375 calories | 11F | 50C | 20P
• Mini Calexico
370 calories | 13F | 41C | 22P

• Mini Maddy, add chicken
380 calories | 10F | 40C | 30P

Panda Express
• Grilled Teriyaki Chicken 6oz
+ Mixed Veggies
378 calories | 13.5F | 24C | 40P
• Grilled Asian Chicken 6oz
+ Mixed Veggies
378 calories | 13.5F | 24C | 40P
• String Bean Chicken 5.6oz
+ Mixed Veggies
274 calories | 9.5F | 29C | 18P

PDQ
• Classic Salad, Grilled Chicken
270 calories | 11F | 11C | 34P
• Grilled Chicken Tenders, 3ct.
180 calories | 2F | 12C | 31P
• Cali Club Sandwich, Lettuce Wrap
300 calories | 13F | 17C | 33P
• Grilled Cali Bowl, No Rice
430 calories | 15F | 40C | 37P
• Grilled Chicken Sandwich, Brioche Bun w/Honey Mustard
400 calories | 13F | 39C | 31P

Pei Wei
(omit rice and noodles in all entrees)
• Small Sesame Chicken salad or lettuce wrapped:
410 calories | 13F | 44C | 26P
• Small Sweet n' Sour Chicken salad or lettuce wrapped:
290 calories | 3F | 42C | 24P
• Small Mongolian Chicken salad or lettuce wrapped:
330 calories | 13F | 30C | 23P
• Small Thai Dynamite Chicken salad or lettuce wrapped:
280 calories | 8F | 25C | 26P
• Regular Lemon Pepper Chicken salad or lettuce wrapped:
400 calories | 4.5F | 44C | 43P

Panera Bread

- Mediterranean Scrambled Egg White Wrap
270 calories | 8F | 33C | 20P
- Greek Yogurt w/Mixed Berries
300 calories | 10F | 39C | 14P
- Mediterranean Scrambled Strawberry Poppyseed Salad
210 calories | 11F | 28C | 20P
- Seasonal Greens Salad w/Chicken
255 calories | 12F | 20C | 20.5P
- Lentil Quinoa Broth Bowl w/Chicken
380 calories | 8F | 45C | 32P
- Soba Noodle Broth Bowl w/Chicken
360 calories | 9F | 43C | 28P

Pizzeria Limone

- Caesar Salad, Full + chicken w/ 2 oz. Lemon Vinaigrette Dressing
400 calories | 18F | 37C | 23P
- Tre Sorelle Salad, half + chicken w/ 2 oz. Lemon Vinaigrette Dressing
395 calories | 18F | 37C | 21P
- Viola Pizza - ½ pizza
410 calories | 16F | 48C | 18P
- Verdure Pizza - ½ pizza
395 calories | 15F | 50C | 15P

Potbelly Sandwich Shop

- Farmhouse Salad
321 calories | 15F | 11C | 35P
- Skinny T-K-Y
294 calories | 6F | 40C | 22P
- Buffalo Grilled Chicken Sandwich on multigrain wheat
332 calories | 11F | 39C | 21P
- Skinny Beef Sandwich on multigrain ThinCut wheat
340 calories | 10F | 39C | 22P
- Turkey Breast Sandwich on multigrain wheat
442 calories | 11F | 58C | 36P

Protein Foundry

- Lush Shake Out, 16 oz.
325 calories | 8F | 37C | 29P
- Raspberry Cheesecake Shake Out, 16 oz.
330 calories | 8F | 36C | 30P
- Super M(atcha) Shake Out, 16 oz.
340 calories | 5F | 49C | 29P
- Aphrodite Bowl, vanilla
325 calories | 8F | 52C | 17P
- Athena Bowl, vanilla
360 calories | 11F | 52C | 18P

Protein House

- SHRDD Veggie Omelette w/side fruit
261 calories | 7F | 32C | 23P
- Super Bird Omelette w/side fruit
307 calories | 7F | 23C | 39P
- Hulk Protein Shake
430 calories | 11F | 56C | 31P
- Apple Butter Shake
463 calories | 12F | 54C | 31P
- Vanilla Gorilla Frap
313 calories | 10F | 28C | 26P
- Mocha Loca Frap
310 calories | 10F | 27C | 29P
- Aloha Burger (whole wheat bun)
401 calories | 7F | 42C | 46P
- Portobello Sandwich
264 calories | 5F | 13C | 44P

Shake Shack

- Burger Patty on gluten-free bun, no cheese, add ketchup and veggies of choice
360 calories | 15.5F | 32C | 21P
- Burger Patty on lettuce wrap, no cheese, add ketchup and veggies of choice
196 calories | 12F | 2C | 20P
- Chicken Bites
300 calories | 15F | 18C | 22P
- Chicken Dog
310 calories | 13F | 27C | 24P
- Chicken Shack-Cago Dog
330 calories | 13F | 31C | 24P

Starbucks

- Blueberry Muesli & Yogurt Bowl
310 calories | 1.5F | 57C | 17P
- Blueberries & Honey Greek Yogurt Parfait
240 calories | 2.5F | 42C | 14P
- Lemon Crunch Yogurt Parfait
340 calories | 13F | 38C | 18P
- Berry Trio Parfait
240 calories | 2.5F | 39C | 14P
- Mango & Coconut Yogurt Bowl
290 calories | 6F | 57C | 12P
- Classic Oatmeal + 1 serving CSE Protein
270 calories | 2.5F | 37C | 25P
- Hearty Blueberry Oatmeal + 1 serving CSE Simply Vanilla Protein
330 calories | 2.5F | 52C | 25P
- Bacon Gouda & Egg Sandwich
370 calories | 19F | 32C | 18P
- Spinach Feta & Egg White Wrap
290 calories | 10F | 33C | 19P
- Ham & Cheese Croissant
320 calories | 17F | 28C | 14P
- Turkey Bacon & Egg White Breakfast Sandwich
220 calories | 5F | 26C | 18P
- Tomato & Mozzarella Sandwich
350 calories | 13F | 42C | 15P
- Honey BBQ Sriracha Chicken Sandwich
370 calories | 8F | 54C | 22P
- Chicken & Quinoa Protein Bowl
420 calories | 17F | 42C | 27P
- Za'atar Chicken & Lemon Tahini Salad
430 calories | 21F | 42C | 21P
- Seasoned Turkey & Green Pepper Pico Salad
390 calories | 18F | 30C | 28P
- Cage-Free Eggs & Seasoned Grains Side Salad
360 calories | 18F | 33C | 17P

Subway

- 3" Egg White Sandwich, double egg whites, Artisan Flatbread, cheddar cheese, avocado
244 calories | 8F | 23C | 20P
- 6" Oven Roasted Chicken Breast Sandwich, honey wheat bread, provolone cheese, veggies, mustard, salt & pepper
320 calories | 7F | 40C | 27P
- 6" Sweet Onion Chicken Teriyaki Sandwich, honey wheat bread, swiss cheese, veggies, sweet onion sauce, salt & pepper
360 calories | 8F | 48C | 29P
- 6" Roast Beef Sandwich honey wheat bread, pepper jack cheese, veggies, mustard, salt & pepper
340 calories | 9F | 40C | 29P
- 6" Rotisserie Chicken Sandwich, honey wheat bread, pepper jack cheese, veggies, mustard, salt & pepper
330 calories | 8F | 41C | 25P
- 6" Subway Club Sandwich, honey wheat bread, American cheese, veggies, mustard, salt & pepper
340 calories | 8F | 42C | 26P
- Rotisserie Style Chicken Salad, veggies, feta cheese, Subway Vinaigrette
310 calories | 16F | 14C | 28P

Wendy's

- Parmesan Caesar Chicken Salad (half size)
320 calories | 20F | 9C | 29P
- Apple Pecan Chicken Salad (half size)
340 calories | 17F | 29C | 20P
- Harvest Chicken Salad (half size)
330 calories | 15F | 25C | 22P
- Southwest Avocado Chicken Salad (half size)
310 calories | 21F | 10C | 22P
- Large Chili
250 calories | 6F | 29C | 21P
- Grilled Chicken Wrap
300 calories | 13F | 26C | 20P
- Grilled Chicken Sandwich
380 calories | 10F | 38C | 35P

WEEK 1

MENU PLANNER

	BREAKFAST	SNACK	LUNCH	SNACK	DINNER	*SNACK
MON	Almond Joy Shake P111	Choose from snack options	Autumn Salad Sandwich P141	Choose from snack options	Chicken Enchilada Stuffed Spaghetti Squash P143	*Choose from snack options
TUES	Almond Joy Shake	Choose from snack options	Chicken Enchilada Stuffed Spaghetti Squash	Choose from snack options	Taco Soup P145	*Choose from snack options
WED	Almond Joy Shake	Choose from snack options	Taco Soup	Choose from snack options	Harvest Cobb Salad P147	*Choose from snack options
THURS	Almond Joy Shake	Choose from snack options	Harvest Cobb Salad	Choose from snack options	Parmesan Crusted Salmon P149	*Choose from snack options
FRI	Almond Joy Shake	Choose from snack options	Parmesan Crusted Salmon	Choose from snack options	DINE OUT	N/A
SAT	Apple Cinnamon Protein Pancakes P113	Choose from snack options	Autumn Salad Sandwich	Choose from snack options	Pepperoni Pizza Pinwheels P151	*Choose from snack options
SUN	Apple Cinnamon Protein Pancakes	Choose from snack options	Pepperoni Pizza Pinwheels	Choose from snack options	BBQ Beef Sandwich & Slaw P153	*Choose from snack options

*Be sure this snack fits into your daily calorie allotment.

PRODUCE
Apples, 3
Apples or Pears, 3
Avocados, 3
Bananas, 7
Broccoli Florets, 8 cups
Coleslaw Mix, 2 cups
Garlic, Minced, 1 tsp.
Green Onions, 1 bunch
Kale, Baby, Chopped, 4 cups
Lemons, 2,
Onion, Red, 1
Onion, Yellow, 1
Parsley, 1 bunch
Squash, Butternut, 4 cups cubed
Squash, Spaghetti, 1
Spinach, Chopped, 8 Cups

MEAT & SEAFOOD
Beef Brisket or Roast, Lean, 8 oz. (½ lb.)
Chicken Breasts, 26 oz.
Ground Turkey, Lean, 8 oz. (½ lb.)
Salmon, Wild Caught, 12 oz. (¾ lb.)
Turkey Bacon, 4 slices

REFRIGERATED
Almond Milk, Unsweetened, 10 ¾ cups
Cheese, Mozzarella, Shredded, Low-fat,
    2 ¼ cups
Cheese, Parmesan, Finely Grated, ¼ cup
Eggs, Large, 6
Egg Whites, 2 (¼ cup liquid)
Greek Yogurt, Plain, Nonfat, 2 cups
Laughing Cow Cheese Wedges, Lite, 4
Turkey Pepperoni, 2 oz.

PANTRY
Apple Cider Vinegar, 4 tsp.
Baking Powder, 1 tsp.
Black Beans, 1 ½ cup
Breadcrumbs, Whole Grain, ¼ cup
Cashews, Chopped, ¼ cup
Cocoa Powder, ⅔ cup + 2 Tbs.
CSE Brownie Batter Protein Powder,
    10 servings
CSE Maple Syrup, Liquid, ½ cup
CSE Simply Vanilla Protein Powder,
    1 serving
CSE Vanilla Pancake & Waffle Mix,
    1 ¼ cups

Enchilada Sauce, Red or Green, 1 cup
Flour, White Whole Wheat, ¾ cup
Green Chiles, Canned, Chopped, 4 oz.
Honey, Raw, 2 Tbs.
Marinara Sauce, ½ cup
Mayo, Olive Oil, 6 Tbs.
Mayo, Low-Fat, ½ cup
Mustard, Dijon, 2 Tbs.
Nutritional Yeast Flakes, 4 Tbs.
Oats, Rolled, Old-Fashioned, 1 ¼ cups
OffBeat Midnight Almond Coconut Butter
    or Natural Almond Butter, 5 Tbs.
Olive Oil, 2 Tbs.
Pecans, Chopped, ¾ cup
Quinoa, Dry, 1 cup
Shredded Coconut, Unsweetened
    ⅔ cup + 2 Tbs.
Stubb's BBQ Sauce, any variety, ¼ cup
Tomatoes, Canned, Crushed, 16 oz.

SWEETENERS, SEASONINGS & SPICES
Black Pepper, dash of
Celery Seed, dash of
Cinnamon, 1 tsp.
Coconut Extract, 5 tsp.
Garlic Powder, dash of
Mustard, Dry, 1 tsp.
Nutmeg, ½ tsp.
Onion Powder, dash of
Sea Salt, dash of
Stevia, dash of
Taco Seasoning, 2 Tbs.
Thyme, dash of
Vanilla Extract, 7 tsp.

FROZEN
Corn, Yellow, Sweet, 1 cup
Ezekiel Bread, 4 slices
Ezekiel English Muffins, 4

OTHER
Cooking Spray
Parchment Paper
Zip Top Bags, Large

Remember to purchase ingredients for your selected weekly snacks!

WEEK 2

MENU PLANNER

	BREAKFAST	SNACK	LUNCH	SNACK	DINNER	*SNACK
MON	Pumpkin Pie Overnight Oats P115	Choose from snack options	BBQ Beef Sandwiches P153	Choose from snack options	Chicken Fettuccine Alfredo P155	*Choose from snack options
TUES	Pumpkin Pie Overnight Oats	Choose from snack options	Chicken Fettuccine Alfredo	Choose from snack options	Honey Garlic Chicken Tacos P157	*Choose from snack options
WED	Pumpkin Pie Overnight Oats	Choose from snack options	Honey Garlic Chicken Tacos	Choose from snack options	Open-Faced Tuna Melt P159	*Choose from snack options
THURS	Pumpkin Pie Overnight Oats	Choose from snack options	Open-Faced Tuna Melt	Choose from snack options	Grilled Cheese & Tomato Soup P161	*Choose from snack options
FRI	Pumpkin Pie Overnight Oats	Choose from snack options	Grilled Cheese & Tomato Soup	Choose from snack options	DINE OUT	N/A
SAT	Breakfast Burritos P117	Choose from snack options	FAST FOOD MACROS LIST	Choose from snack options	Thai Chicken Pizza P163	*Choose from snack options
SUN	Breakfast Burritos	Choose from snack options	Thai Chicken Pizza	Choose from snack options	Turkey Pot Pies P165	*Choose from snack options

*Be sure this snack fits into your daily calorie allotment.

20

PRODUCE
Avocado, 1
Basil, 1 package
Bell Pepper, Green, 1
Cabbage, Green, Chopped, 1 cup
Carrots, 4 small
Carrots, Matchstick, 2 oz.
Cauliflower Florets, 2 cups
Celery, 10 sticks
Cilantro, 1 bunch
Garlic, Cloves, 8
Green Onions, 1 bunch
Lemon, 1
Lime, 1
Onion, Red, 1
Onion, Yellow, 1
Parsley, Flat-Leaf, Minced, 1 Tbs.
Potatoes, Red, 4 oz.
Shallot, 1
Spinach, Chopped, 4 ½ cups
Tomatoes, Cherry, 12
Tomatoes, Vine, 2

MEAT & SEAFOOD
Chicken Breasts, 28 oz.
Chicken Sausage, Sugarhouse Maple,
   AMYLU, 4 small links (30 cals each)
Turkey Breast, Roasted, 8 oz. (½ lb.)
Turkey, Deli, Nitrate-free, 10 oz. (~⅔ lb.)

REFRIGERATED
Almond Milk, Unsweetened, 6 ¼ cups
Butter, Grass-fed, 3 Tbs.
Cheese, Cheddar, Low-fat, Shredded,
   ¾ cup
Cheese, Mozzarella, Low-fat, Shredded,
   2 cups
Cheese, Parmesan, Grated, ¼ cup
Eggs, Large, 4
Egg Whites, 8 (1 cup liquid egg whites)
Greek Yogurt, Plain, Nonfat, 1 ¼ cup
Spray Whipped Cream, 1 ¼ cups

PANTRY
Almond Butter, Natural, ½ cup
Cashews, ½ cup

Chicken Bone Broth, Low-Sodium,1 ¾ cups
Coconut Aminos or Soy Sauce,1 tsp.
Coconut Milk, Light, Canned, ½ cup
Coconut Oil, 1 Tbs.
CSE Buttermilk Pancake & Waffle Mix,
   3 ¼ cups
CSE Simply Vanilla Protein Powder,
   7 ½ servings
Fettuccine, Whole Wheat, Dry, 5 oz.
Honey, Raw, 3 Tbs.
Marinara Sauce, ½ cup
Mayo, Olive Oil, 2 Tbs.
Nutritional Yeast Flakes, 2 Tbs.
English Muffins, Multigrain, 4
Oats, Rolled, Old-fashioned, 3 ¾ cups
Olive Oil, 6 Tbs.
OffBeat Sweet Classic Peanut Butter,
   or Natural Peanut Butter, 1 Tbs.
Pecans, Chopped, 10 tsp.
Pumpkin, Canned, 1 ¼ cups
Salsa, 2 cups
Sriracha Sauce, 1 tsp.
Tomatoes, Canned, Fire Roasted, Diced,
   28 oz.
Tortillas, Corn, 8
Tortillas, Whole Grain (120 cals each), 4
Tuna, Canned, Chunk Light, 10 oz.
   weight after drained

SWEETENERS, SEASONINGS & SPICES
Bay Leaves, 2
Black Pepper, 3 Tbs.
Garlic Powder, dash of
Onion Powder, dash of
Pumpkin Pie Spice, 5 tsp.
Sea Salt, 3 Tbs.
Stevia in the Raw, 1 tsp.
Taco Seasoning, 1 ½ Tbs.

FROZEN
Peas, ½ cup
Sprouted Grain Ezekiel Bread, 4 slices

OTHER
Cooking Spray
Parchment Paper
Zip Top Bags, Large

Remember to purchase ingredients for your selected weekly snacks!

WEEK 3

MENU PLANNER

	BREAKFAST	SNACK	LUNCH	SNACK	DINNER	*SNACK
MON	Hot Apple Pie Oats P119	Choose from snack options	Turkey Pot Pies P165	Choose from snack options	Thai Peanut Spaghetti P167	*Choose from snack options
TUES	Hot Apple Pie Oats	Choose from snack options	Thai Peanut Spaghetti	Choose from snack options	Salsa Verde Chicken Burritos P169	*Choose from snack options
WED	Hot Apple Pie Oats	Choose from snack options	Salsa Verde Chicken Burritos	Choose from snack options	Beef & Broccoli Stir-Fry P171	*Choose from snack options
THURS	Hot Apple Pie Oats	Choose from snack options	Beef & Broccoli Stir-Fry	Choose from snack options	Cranberry, Pear & Turkey Salad P173	*Choose from snack options
FRI	Hot Apple Pie Oats	Choose from snack options	Cranberry, Pear & Turkey Salad	Choose from snack options	DINE OUT	N/A
SAT	Pumpkin Protein Waffles P121	Choose from snack options	FAST FOOD MACROS LIST	Choose from snack options	Garden Veggie Pizza P175	*Choose from snack options
SUN	Pumpkin Protein Waffles	Choose from snack options	Garden Veggie Pizza	Choose from snack options	Thai Protein Bowl P177	*Choose from snack options

*Be sure this snack fits into your daily calorie allotment.

WEEK 3 GROCERY LIST | Serves 2 adults for the week

PRODUCE
Apples, 5
Avocado, 1
Bell Pepper, Yellow, 2
Broccoli, Chopped, 6 cups
Cabbage, Green, Shredded, 1 cup
Carrots, Matchstick, 1 cup
Cilantro, 1 bunch
Cucumber, 1
Garlic, Minced, 1 clove
Green Onions, 1 bunch
Kale, Baby, Chopped, 8 cups
Lemon, 1
Lettuce, Shredded, 4 cups
Mushrooms, Sliced, ½ cup
Onions, Red, 2
Pears, 3
Shallots, 2
Spinach, 8 cups
Sugar Snap Peas, 2 cups
Tomato, Vine, 1

MEAT & SEAFOOD
Chicken Breast, 29 oz. raw
Chicken Sausage Links, Large, 2
    (160 cals each / Aidells, Applegate,
    Coleman, Simple Truth)
Steak, Sirloin Tip, 16 oz.
Turkey Breast, Roasted, Chopped, 12 oz.

REFRIGERATED
Almond Milk, Unsweetened, ½ cup
Bolthouse Cilantro Avocado Dressing,
    ¼ cup
Butter, Grass-fed, ¼ cup
Cheese, Mozzarella, Low-fat, Shredded,
    1 ½ cups
Eggs, Large, 2
Egg Whites, 20 (or 2 ½ cups liquid)
Greek Yogurt, Plain, Nonfat, 1 ¾ cups
Spray Whipped Cream, ½ cup

PANTRY
Apple Cider Vinegar, 1 Tbs.
Artichoke Hearts, Canned, ½ cup
Baking Powder, 1 tsp.
Chia Seeds, 1 tsp.
Coconut Aminos or Soy Sauce, 6 Tbs.

Cashews, 6 oz.
Cranberries, Dried, Unsweetened, 1 cup
CSE Maple Syrup, Liquid, ¼ cup
CSE Simply Vanilla Protein Powder,
    7 servings
CSE Vanilla Pancake & Waffle Mix, 1 cup
Flour, White Whole Wheat, ¾ cup
Honey, Raw, 6 Tbs.
Marinara Sauce, Traditional, ¾ cup
Oats, Rolled, Old-fashioned, 3 ⅓ cups
OffBeat Cinnamon Bun Butter, or
    Natural Almond Butter, 1 ¼ cups
OffBeat Salted Caramel Butter, or
    Natural Almond Butter, 4 Tbs.
OffBeat Sweet Classic Peanut Butter, or
    Natural Peanut Butter, 5 Tbs.
Olives, Canned, Sliced, ½ cup
Olive Oil, 5 Tbs.
Peanuts, Chopped, ½ oz.
Pumpkin, Canned, ½ cup
Pumpkin Seeds, Shelled, ¼ cup
Quinoa, Dry, ¼ cup
Rice Vinegar, 3 tsp.
Rice, White, Jasmine, Dry, 3 Tbs.
Salsa, ½ cup
Salsa Verde Green Salsa, 1 cup
Spaghetti, Whole Grain, 4 oz. uncooked
Tortillas, Whole Grain, 4 (120 cals each)
Water Chestnuts, 2 cups

SWEETENERS, SEASONINGS & SPICES
Black Pepper, dash of
Cayenne Pepper, dash of
Cinnamon, dash of
Garlic Powder, dash of
Mustard, Dry, dash of
Nutmeg, dash of
Onion Powder, dash of
Oregano, dash of
Pumpkin Pie Spice, 2 tsp.
Sea salt, dash of
Vanilla Stevia Drops

OTHER
Cooking Spray
Parchment Paper

Remember to purchase ingredients for your selected weekly snacks!

WEEK 4

MENU PLANNER

	BREAKFAST	SNACK	LUNCH	SNACK	DINNER	*SNACK
MON	Superfood Cereal P123	Choose from snack options	Thai Protein Bowl P177	Choose from snack options	Grilled Caprese Panini P179	*Choose from snack options
TUES	Superfood Cereal	Choose from snack options	Grilled Caprese Panini	Choose from snack options	Salsa Chicken Pile-Up P181	*Choose from snack options
WED	Superfood Cereal	Choose from snack options	Salsa Chicken Pile-Up	Choose from snack options	Roasted Butternut Squash Soup P183	*Choose from snack options
THURS	Superfood Cereal	Choose from snack options	Roasted Butternut Squash Soup	Choose from snack options	Maple Pecan Glazed Salmon P185	*Choose from snack options
FRI	Superfood Cereal	Choose from snack options	Maple Pecan Glazed Salmon	Choose from snack options	DINE OUT	N/A
SAT	Bacon, Egg & Avocado Sandwich P125	Choose from snack options	FAST FOOD MACROS LIST	Choose from snack options	Creamy Chicken Corn Chowder P187	*Choose from snack options
SUN	Bacon, Egg & Avocado Sandwich	Choose from snack options	Creamy Chicken Corn Chowder	Choose from snack options	Shepherd's Pie P189	*Choose from snack options

*Be sure this snack fits into your daily calorie allotment.

WEEK 4 GROCERY LIST | Serves 2 adults for the week

PRODUCE
Avocado, 1
Basil, Fresh, 1 bunch
Bell Pepper, Red, 2
Blueberries, 1 ¼ cups
Broccoli, 4 cups
Carrot, Medium, 1
Celery, 1 stick
Chives, 1 package
Garlic, Cloves, 4
Green Onions, 1 bunch
Jalapeños, 2
Kale, Baby, 1 cup
Lemon, 1, juice of
Lettuce, Shredded, 4 cups
Onion, Yellow, 2
Potatoes, Red, 23 oz.
Potatoes, Sweet, 24 oz.
Spring Mix Greens, 2 cups
Squash, Butternut, 8 oz.
Tomatoes, 4 (12 slices)

MEAT & SEAFOOD
Chicken Breasts, 26 oz.
Salmon, Wild Caught, 12 oz.
Turkey, Lean, Ground, 12 oz.
Turkey Bacon, 20 slices

REFRIGERATED
Almond Milk, Unsweetened, 7 ½ cups
Butter, Grass-fed, 2 Tbs.
Cheese, Cheddar, Shredded, Sharp,
  ½ cup
Cheese, Mozzarella, Shredded, Low-Fat,
  1 cup
Cheese, Mozzarella, Sliced, Fresh, 5 oz.
Eggs, Large, 4
Egg Whites, 8 (1 cup liquid egg whites)
Greek Yogurt, Nonfat, Plain, 1 ½ cups
Guacamole, 4 oz.

PANTRY
Almonds, Sliced, 1 ¼ cups

Balsamic Glaze, 2 Tbs.
  (typically found by the olive oil)
Black Beans, ½ cup
Cashews, ½ cup
Chia Seeds, ¼ cup
Chicken Broth, Low-Sodium, 3 cups
CSE Buttermilk Pancake & Waffle Mix, 2 Tbs.
CSE Simply Vanilla Protein Powder,
  5 servings
English Muffins, Multigrain, 4
Kashi GO Original Cereal, 7 ½ cups
Olives, Black, Canned, ½ cup
Olive Oil, 1 ½ Tbs.
Pecans, Chopped, 4 Tbs.
Pure Maple Syrup, 2 Tbs.
Rice, (White, Brown or Jasmine), 3 Tbs.
  uncooked
Salsa, 1 cup
Stonefire Naan Bread, Large, 3 pieces
Tomato Paste, ½ cup
Worcestershire Sauce, 4 tsp.

SWEETENERS, SEASONINGS & SPICES
Bay Leaves, 2
Black Pepper, dash of
Cinnamon, dash of
Ginger, Ground, dash of
Paprika, dash of
Sea Salt, dash of
Stevia in the Raw, 1 tsp.

FROZEN
Corn, Yellow, Sweet, 2 cups (or fresh)
Green Beans, 3 cups (or fresh)

OTHER
Cooking Spray
Parchment Paper
Zip Top Bags

Remember to purchase ingredients for your selected weekly snacks!

WEEK 5

MENU PLANNER

	BREAKFAST	SNACK	LUNCH	SNACK	DINNER	*SNACK
MON	Double Chocolate PB Oatmeal P127	Choose from snack options	Shepherd's Pie P189	Choose from snack options	Butternut Squash & Sausage Risotto P191	*Choose from snack options
TUES	Double Chocolate PB Oatmeal	Choose from snack options	Butternut Squash & Sausage Risotto	Choose from snack options	BBQ Chicken Avocado Wrap P193	*Choose from snack options
WED	Double Chocolate PB Oatmeal	Choose from snack options	BBQ Chicken Avocado Wrap	Choose from snack options	Caprese Pasta Bowl P195	*Choose from snack options
THURS	Double Chocolate PB Oatmeal	Choose from snack options	Caprese Pasta Bowl	Choose from snack options	Thai Chicken Soup P197	*Choose from snack options
FRI	Double Chocolate PB Oatmeal	Choose from snack options	Thai Chicken Soup	Choose from snack options	DINE OUT	N/A
SAT	Apple Butter Crepes P129	Choose from snack options	FAST FOOD MACROS LIST	Choose from snack options	Maple Dijon Protein Bowl P199	*Choose from snack options
SUN	Apple Butter Crepes	Choose from snack options	Maple Dijon Protein Bowl	Choose from snack options	Cheddar Ranch Chicken & Potatoes P201	*Choose from snack options

*Be sure this snack fits into your daily calorie allotment.

WEEK 5 GROCERY LIST | Serves 2 adults for the week

PRODUCE
Apples, 2
Avocado, 2
Banana, 4
Basil, 1 bunch
Bell Pepper, Red, 1
Bell Pepper, Yellow, 1
Broccoli, 6 cups
Butter Lettuce, 1 head/container
Carrots, Chopped, 1 cup
Cilantro, 1 bunch
Garlic, Cloves, 3
Ginger, Fresh, Grated, 2 tsp.
Green Onions, 1 bunch
Lime, 1
Onion, Red, 1
Onion, Yellow, 1
Potatoes, Baby Gold, 20 oz.
Salad Mix Greens, 4 cups
Shallot, 1
Squash, Butternut, 2 cups
Spinach, 4 cups
Tomatoes, Vine, 2 (8 slices)
Tomatoes, Cherry, 1 cup

MEAT & SEAFOOD
Chicken Breast, 43 oz.
Chicken Sausage, Italian flavored, 2
   (160 cals each / Aidells, Applegate,
   Coleman, Simple Truth)
Steak, Sirloin Tip, 12 oz.
Turkey, Lean, Ground, 10 oz.

REFRIGERATED
Almond Milk, Unsweetened, 1 ½ cups
Butter, Grass-fed, 1 Tbs.
Cheese, Mozzarella, Pearls, 4 oz.
Cheese, Parmesan, Grated, 4 Tbs.
Cheese, Cheddar, Low-Fat, Shredded,
   1 cup
Egg, Large, 2
Egg Whites, 6 (2 ¾ cup liquid)
Greek Yogurt, Plain, Nonfat, 1 cup

PANTRY
Avocado Oil, 2 Tbs.
   (or light tasting olive oil)

Balsamic Glaze, 2 Tbs.
   (typically found by the olive oil)
Balsamic Vinegar, 2 Tbs.
Chicken Stock, Low-Sodium, 1 cup
Coconut Milk, Light, Canned, 1 ½ cups
Coconut Oil, ½ Tbs.
CSE Brownie Batter Protein Powder,
   5 servings
CSE Buttermilk Pancake & Waffle Mix, 1 Tbs.
CSE Maple Syrup, Liquid, 4 Tbs.
CSE Simply Vanilla Protein Powder,
   ½ serving
CSE Vanilla Pancake & Waffle Mix, 1 cup
Fish Sauce, 1 Tbs.
Flatout Wraps or
   Joseph's Flatbread Wraps, 4
Honey, Raw, 1 Tbs.
Mustard, Dijon, 2 tsp.
Oats, Rolled, Old-fashioned, 3 ⅓ cups
OffBeat Buckeye Brownie Peanut Butter,
   10 Tbs. (or 140g Dark Chocolate Chips)
OffBeat Cinnamon Bun, Salted Caramel
   Butter, or Natural Almond Butter, ¼ cup
OffBeat Powdered Peanut Butter, 10 Tbs.
OffBeat Sweet Classic Peanut Butter, or
   Natural Peanut Butter, 7 Tbs.
Penne Pasta, Brown Rice, Dry, 5 oz.
Pure Maple Syrup, 2 Tbs.
Quinoa, Dry, 1 cup
Ranch DIPS Powder, 2 tsp.
Red Curry Paste, 1 Tbs.
Rice, White, Jasmine, Dry, 1 cup + 2 Tbs.
Stubb's Original BBQ Sauce, ½ cup
Vegetable Stock, 1½ cups

SWEETENERS, SEASONINGS & SPICES
Black Pepper, dash of
Cinnamon, 3 tsp.
Sea Salt, dash of
Stevia in the Raw, 1 tsp.

OTHER
Cooking Spray
Parchment Paper

Remember to purchase ingredients for your selected weekly snacks!

	BREAKFAST	SNACK	LUNCH	SNACK	DINNER	*SNACK
MON	Pumpkin French Toast P131	Choose from snack options	Cheddar Ranch Chicken & Potatoes P201	Choose from snack options	Tomato Basil Spaghetti & Meatballs P203	*Choose from snack options
TUES	Pumpkin French Toast	Choose from snack options	Tomato Basil Spaghetti & Meatballs	Choose from snack options	Fall Maple Hash P205	*Choose from snack options
WED	Pumpkin French Toast	Choose from snack options	Fall Maple Hash	Choose from snack options	Sloppy Sweet Potato P207	*Choose from snack options
THURS	Pumpkin French Toast	Choose from snack options	Sloppy Sweet Potato	Choose from snack options	Mediterranean Bounty Bowl P209	*Choose from snack options
FRI	Pumpkin French Toast	Choose from snack options	Mediterranean Bounty Bowl	Choose from snack options	DINE OUT	N/A
SAT	One Pan Country Skillet P133	Choose from snack options	FAST FOOD MACROS LIST	Choose from snack options	Cheesy Roasted Veggies & Sausage P211	*Choose from snack options
SUN	One Pan Country Skillet	Choose from snack options	Cheesy Roasted Veggies & Sausage	Choose from snack options	White Chicken Chili P213	*Choose from snack options

*Be sure this snack fits into your daily calorie allotment.

PRODUCE
Avocado, 2
Basil, Fresh, 1 bunch
Bell Peppers, Mini, Variety, 12
Broccoli, 4 cups
Brussel Sprouts, 4 cups
Cilantro, 1 bunch
Cucumbers, 2 cups
Garlic, Cloves, 3
Green Onions, 1 bunch
Jalapeño, 1
Lime, 1
Mushrooms, 1 cup chopped
Onion, Yellow, 4
Potatoes, Sweet, White, 14 oz.
Potatoes, Red (or Sweet Potatoes), 24 oz.
Spinach, Chopped, 6 cups
Squash, Acorn, 4 cups
Squash, Butternut, 24 oz.
Squash, Spaghetti, 2
Tomatoes, Cherry, 20

MEAT & SEAFOOD
Chicken Breasts, 14 oz.
Chicken Sausages, Large, 6 (Aidells, Applegate, Coleman, Simple Truth)
Chicken Sausage, Sugarhouse Maple, AMYLU, 18 small links (30 cals each)
Rotisserie Chicken, 10 oz. cooked
Turkey, Lean, Ground, 40 oz.

REFRIGERATED
Almond Milk, Unsweetened, ¾ cup
Bolthouse Farms Italian Vinaigrette Dressing, 120g (about ½ cup)
Butter, Grass-fed, 1 Tbs.
Cheese, Cheddar, Shredded, Low-fat, 4 Tbs.
Cheese, Parmesan, Grated, ¼ cup
Cottage Cheese, Low-fat, 2 ½ cups
Eggs, Large, 14
Egg Whites, 2 (¼ cup liquid egg whites)
Greek Yogurt, Plain, Nonfat, ½ cup
Hummus, 4 Tbs.
Kalamata Olives, Pitted, 20
Laughing Cow Cheese, Garlic and Herb, 4 wedges

PANTRY
Almonds, Slivered, ¼ cup
Apple Cider Vinegar, 2 tsp.
Arrowroot Starch, 1 Tbs. (or corn starch)
Chicken Stock, Low-Sodium, 1 ½ cups
CSE Maple Syrup, optional
Great Northern White Beans, 1 cup
Green Chiles, Diced, Canned, 4 oz.
Honey, Raw, 2 Tbs.
Pecans, Chopped, 10 Tbs.
Pumpkin, Canned, 1 ¼ cups
Pure Maple Syrup, 1 Tbs.
Quinoa, Dry, ¼ cup
Salsa, ½ cup
Tomatoes, Crushed, Canned, ½ cup
Tomatoes, Diced, Canned (or Fresh), 28 oz.
Tortillas, Corn, 4
Worcestershire Sauce, 1 Tbs.

SWEETENERS, SEASONINGS & SPICES
Black Pepper, dash of
Chili Powder, 1 ½ tsp.
Cinnamon, dash of
Coriander, 1 tsp.
Cumin, Ground, 4 tsp.
Garlic Powder, dash of
Onion Powder, dash of
Oregano, Dried, ¼ tsp.
Pumpkin Pie Spice, 2 ½ tsp.
Sea Salt, dash of
Vanilla Extract, 2 ½ tsp.
Vanilla Stevia Drops, to taste

FROZEN
Corn, Yellow, Sweet, ½ cup
Green Beans, 4 cups (or Fresh)
Sprouted Grain Ezekiel Bread, 23 slices

OTHER
Cooking Spray
Parchment Paper
Zip Top Bags, Large

Remember to purchase ingredients for your selected weekly snacks!

WEEK 7

MENU PLANNER

	BREAKFAST	SNACK	LUNCH	SNACK	DINNER	*SNACK
MON	Cinna-Berry Breakfast Squares P135	Choose from snack options	White Chicken Chili P213	Choose from snack options	BLTA Waffle Sandwich P215	*Choose from snack options
TUES	Cinna-Berry Breakfast Squares	Choose from snack options	BLTA Waffle Sandwich	Choose from snack options	Stacked Chicken Enchiladas P217	*Choose from snack options
WED	Cinna-Berry Breakfast Squares	Choose from snack options	Stacked Chicken Enchiladas	Choose from snack options	Pesto Chicken Sliders P219	*Choose from snack options
THURS	Cinna-Berry Breakfast Squares	Choose from snack options	Pesto Chicken Sliders	Choose from snack options	Philly Cheesesteak Wraps P221	*Choose from snack options
FRI	Cinna-Berry Breakfast Squares	Choose from snack options	Philly Cheesesteak Wraps	Choose from snack options	DINE OUT	N/A
SAT	Lemon Raspberry Crepes P137	Choose from snack options	FAST FOOD MACROS LIST	Choose from snack options	Buffalo Chicken & Mozzarella Meatballs P223	*Choose from snack options
SUN	Lemon Raspberry Crepes	Choose from snack options	Buffalo Chicken & Mozzarella Meatballs	Choose from snack options	Chinese Sesame Chicken P225	*Choose from snack options

*Be sure this snack fits into your daily calorie allotment.

WEEK 7 GROCERY LIST | Serves 2 adults for the week

PRODUCE
Avocado, 2
Bananas, 5
Bell Pepper, Green, 1
Bell Pepper, Red, 2
Blackberries, ½ cup
Blueberries, 1 cup
Broccolini, 4 cups
Carrot Sticks, 8 oz.
Celery Sticks, 8 sticks
Garlic, Cloves, 2
Ginger, Fresh, Grated, 1 Tbs.
Green Leaf Lettuce, 1 head
Green Onions, Chopped, 1 bunch
Onions, Yellow, 2
Pico De Gallo, 4 Tbs.
Potatoes, Red, 14 oz.
Potatoes, Sweet, 18 oz.
Raspberries, 3 cups
Spinach, 1 cup
Tomato, Vine, 1

MEAT & SEAFOOD
Chicken Breasts, 30 oz.
Chicken Breast, Ground, 27 oz.
Ribeye Steak, 5 oz.
Turkey Bacon, 8 slices

REFRIGERATED
Almond Milk, Unsweetened, 2 cups
Bolthouse Farms Chunky Bleu Cheese
   Dressing, 4 Tbs. (or Classic Ranch)
Cheese, Cheddar, Shredded, Low-Fat,
   ¼ cup
Cheese, Bleu, Crumbles, 2 Tbs.
   (or feta cheese crumbles)
Cheese, Mozzarella, Shredded, Low- fat,
   ½ cup
Cheese, Provolone, Shredded, ½ cup
Eggs, Large, 19
Egg Whites, 48 (6 cups liquid egg whites)
Greek Yogurt, Plain, Nonfat, 4 Tbs.
   Pesto Sauce, 4 Tbs.
Spray Whipped Cream, 1 ½ cups
String Cheese Sticks, 2

PANTRY
Applesauce, Unsweetened, 2 Tbs.

Arrowroot, 1 Tbs. (or Cornstarch)
Baking Powder, 1 tsp.
Beans, Kidney or Black, ½ cup
Chicken Broth, Low-sodium, ½ cup
Chili Paste, 2 tsp. (or Sriracha Sauce)
Coconut Aminos or Soy Sauce, ¼ cup
Coconut Palm Sugar, ¼ cup
CSE Buttermilk Pancake & Waffle Mix,
   1 ¾ cups
CSE Simply Vanilla Protein Powder,
   3 servings
Enchilada Sauce, Red or Green, 1 ½ cups
Frank's Hot Sauce, ¼ cup
Honey, Raw, ¾ cup
Joseph Flatbread Wraps, 4
Mayo, Olive Oil, 1 Tbs.
Mustard, Dijon, 1 Tbs.
Mustard, Yellow, 1 tsp.
Oats, Rolled, Old-fashioned, 2 ½ cups
OffBeat Lemon Coconut Bliss Butter,
   4 Tbs. or 12 oz. Lemon Noosa Yoghurt
Olive Oil, 1 Tbs.
Panko Breadcrumbs, ¼ cup
Pecans, Chopped, ½ cup
Rice, White, Jasmine, Dry, ¼ cup
Sesame Oil, 2 Tbs.
Sesame Seeds, 4 tsp.
Tortillas, Corn, 6
Vinegar, White Wine, 1 tsp.

SWEETENERS, SEASONINGS & SPICES
Black Pepper, Dash of
Cinnamon, 1 Tbs.
Italian Seasoning, 1 Tbs.
Paprika, Dash of
Sea Salt, Dash of
Taco Seasoning, 1 Tbs.
Vanilla Extract, 2 tsp.

FROZEN
Cauliflower Rice, 16 oz.
Corn, Yellow, Sweet, ½ cup

OTHER
Cooking Spray
Parchment Paper
Zip Top Bags, Large

Remember to purchase ingredients for your selected weekly snacks!

FOOD PREP

GUIDE

WEEK 1 MEAL PREP

SUNDAY PREP
- Prepare daily snacks, if needed.
- Prepare the Almond Joy Shake cups. Layer one serving of the bananas, protein powder, oats, cocoa powder, shredded coconut, almond butter, coconut & vanilla extracts and ice into as many jars as needed for the week. Cover and store in the freezer until ready to use. Dump into the blender with the almond milk. Blend and pour back into the jar to drink.
- Cook chicken for the Autumn Salad Sandwich, Chicken Enchilada Stuffed Spaghetti Squash and the Harvest Cobb Salad.
- Thaw turkey for the Taco Soup.
- Boil the eggs for the Harvest Cobb Salad.
- Chop and cook bacon for the Harvest Cobb Salad.
- Make the Honey Mustard Dressing for the Harvest Cobb Salad.
- Roast butternut squash for the Harvest Cobb Salad.

THURSDAY PREP
- Prepare daily snacks, if needed.
- Cook quinoa for the Parmesan Crusted Salmon.
- Cook chicken for the Autumn Salad Sandwich.
- Thaw beef brisket for the BBQ Beef Sandwiches.

WEEK 2 MEAL PREP

SUNDAY PREP
- Prepare daily snacks, if needed.
- Prepare the Pumpkin Pie Overnight Oats for the week.
- Cook the chicken for the Chicken Fettucine Alfredo.
- Thaw the chicken for the Honey-Garlic Chicken Tacos.
- Prepare the Cashew Sour Cream for the Honey-Garlic Chicken Tacos.

THURSDAY PREP
- Prepare daily snacks, if needed.
- Cook the chicken for the Thai Chicken Pizza.
- Prepare the Thai Peanut Sauce for the Thai Chicken Pizza.
- Make the Breakfast Burritos and store in the freezer. Move to fridge the night before eating.

WEEK 3 MEAL PREP

SUNDAY PREP
- Prepare daily snacks, if needed.
- Prepare Thai Sauce for the Thai Peanut Spaghetti.
- Thaw or cook chicken for the Thai Peanut Spaghetti.
- Thaw Chicken for the Salsa Verde Chicken Burritos.
- Prepare Cashew Sour Cream for the Salsa Verde Chicken Burritos.
- Cook the rice for the Salsa Verde Chicken Burritos.
- Thaw and marinate the beef for the Beef & Broccoli Stir-Fry.

THURSDAY PREP
- Prepare daily snacks, if needed.
- Prepare the dressing for the Cranberry, Pear & Turkey Salad.
- Cook the chicken for the Garden Veggie Pizza and the Thai Protein Bowl.
- Cook the quinoa for the Thai Protein Bowl.

WEEK 4 MEAL PREP

SUNDAY PREP
- Prepare daily snacks, if needed.
- Cook chicken for the Grilled Caprese Panini.
- Cook rice for the Salsa Chicken Pile-Up.
- Prepare Cashew Sour Cream for the Salsa Chicken Pile-Up.
- Peel and cube butternut squash for the Butternut Squash Soup.
- Chop and brown turkey bacon for the Butternut Squash Soup and the Creamy Chicken Corn Chowder.

THURSDAY PREP
- Prepare daily snacks, if needed.
- Thaw salmon for the Maple Pecan Glazed Salmon.
- Thaw or cook chicken for the Creamy Chicken Corn Chowder.
- Thaw turkey for the Shepherd's Pie.

WEEK 5 MEAL PREP

SUNDAY PREP
- Prepare daily snacks, if needed.
- Thaw turkey for the Butternut Squash & Sausage Risotto.
- Peel and cube butternut squash for the Butternut Squash & Sausage Risotto.
- Cook rice in vegetable stock for the Butternut Squash & Sausage Risotto.
- Thaw chicken for the BBQ Chicken Avocado Wrap.
- Thaw or cook chicken for the Caprese Pasta Bowl.

THURSDAY PREP
- Prepare daily snacks, if needed.
- Thaw chicken for the Thai Chicken Soup.
- Cook rice for the Thai Chicken Soup.
- Cook quinoa for the Maple Dijon Protein Bowl.
- Make dressing for the Maple Dijon Protein Bowl.
- Thaw steak for the Maple Dijon Protein Bowl.
- Cook chicken for the Cheddar Ranch Chicken & Potatoes.

WEEK 6 MEAL PREP

SUNDAY PREP
- Prepare daily snacks, if needed.
- Thaw Ezekiel Bread for the Pumpkin French Toast.
- Thaw turkey for the Spaghetti & Meatballs and Sloppy Sweet Potato.
- Peel and cube acorn squash for the Fall Maple Hash.
- Slice Brussels sprouts for the Fall Maple Hash.

THURSDAY PREP
- Prepare daily snacks, if needed.
- Thaw or cook chicken for the Mediterranean Bounty Bowl.
- Peel and cube butternut squash for the Cheesy Roasted Veggies & Sausage.
- Cook the lean ground turkey for the One Pan Country Skillet.
- Cook the potatoes for the One Pan Country Skillet.

WEEK 7 MEAL PREP

SUNDAY PREP
- Prepare daily snacks, if needed.
- Make the Cinna-Berry Breakfast Squares.
- Cook chicken for the Stacked Chicken Enchiladas and Pesto Chicken Sliders.
- Prepare the Honey Mustard Sauce for the BLTA Waffle Sandwich.

THURSDAY PREP
- Prepare daily snacks, if needed.
- Thaw steak for the Philly Cheesesteak Wraps.
- Thaw chicken for the Buffalo Chicken & Mozzarella Meatballs and the Chinese Sesame Chicken.
- Cook the rice and cauliflower rice for the Chinese Sesame Chicken.

CHICKEN

GRILL (whole)
1. Preheat grill to high heat.

2. Make sure chicken is completely thawed out. Butterfly cut chicken breasts (optional, helps them cook faster).

3. Turn heat down to medium, lightly spray grill with non-stick cooking spray and place chicken on grill. Grill about 5-7 minutes per side, flipping occasionally. Chicken is done when it is no longer pink and juices run clear.

4. Season and serve warm or store in the fridge for future use. Use within 3-4 days.

BROIL (whole)
1. Preheat oven to HI broil. Move oven rack to the very top.

2. Spray broiler pan with non-stick cooking spray. Make sure chicken is completely thawed out. Butterfly cut chicken breasts (optional, helps them cook faster) and place on broiler pan.

3. Broil 7-8 minutes per side. Chicken is done when it is no longer pink and juices run clear.

4. Season and serve warm or store in the fridge for future use. Use within 3-4 days.

5. For easy shredding, place in a Kitchen Aid Mixer while warm and mix on low. Hand mixers will work as well.

CROCKPOT (soft, shredded)
1. Place chicken in crockpot with one cup of water, seasonings and/or low-sodium chicken stock.

2. Turn crockpot on low and cook for 5-6 hours OR on high for 3-4 hours. Chicken is done when it is no longer pink and juices run clear. Chicken should be soft and easy to shred.

3. Season and serve warm or store in the fridge for future use. Use within 3-4 days.

INSTANT POT (soft, shredded)
1. Place 2 lbs. of thawed or frozen chicken in the Instant Pot with one cup of water and seasonings or low-sodium chicken stock. If the chicken is frozen, make sure it is broken apart and not frozen in a big clump or it will not cook.

2. Seal lid. Press the manual button and cook on high pressure 9 minutes if thawed and 12 minutes if frozen.

3. The Instant Pot will take a few minutes to heat up and seal before it starts cooking. Let it run its course and once it's done, let it self-vent for 10 minutes. Then manually vent and remove the lid.

4. Season and serve warm or store in the fridge or freezer for future use. Keeps in the fridge 4-5 days and the freezer one month.

SKILLET (cubed)
1. Heat skillet to medium heat and grease with cooking spray. Cube thawed chicken and place in skillet. Season the chicken with salt, pepper and other seasonings of choice. Cover.

2. Stir and flip every three minutes until all sides are golden brown and chicken is cooked through. Place in a sealed container and store in the fridge or freezer.

HOMEMADE BREAD CRUMBS

1. Preheat oven to HI broil. Place slices of bread on a baking sheet lined with parchment paper. Spray tops lightly with cooking spray.

2. Sprinkle with garlic powder. Broil two minutes, flip, then broil another minute. Remove from oven.

3. Place toast in a blender and pulse until broken up into crumbs. Place in a sealed container and store in the fridge.

HARD BOILED EGGS

STOVETOP

1. Place eggs in a pot and fill with water until it covers the eggs.

2. Place pot over high heat and cover. Once water comes to a boil, boil for 2 minutes then remove from heat. Keep covered for 10 minutes.

3. Drain water from pot and run cold water over the top. Transfer the eggs into a separate bowl filled with ice.

4. Once cool, place eggs in a bowl and refrigerate. Peel when ready to eat. Store in the fridge up to 2 weeks.

INSTANT POT

1. Place 6-12 eggs on the rack inside the Instant Pot. Add one cup of water.

2. Cook for 6 minutes on manual. Vent immediately and place eggs into a bowl filled with ice.

3. Once cool, place eggs in a bowl and refrigerate. Peel when ready to eat. Store in the fridge up to 2 weeks.

ROASTED SWEET POTATOES & RED POTATOES

CUBES OR FRIES

1. Preheat oven to 400 degrees. Move oven rack to the center of your oven.

2. Wash and cube or cut sweet potatoes into bite-sized pieces or fries with a sharp knife. Spread out in a single layer onto a baking sheet lined with parchment paper.

3. Spray the tops with cooking spray and sprinkle tops with sea salt and other seasonings of choice. Bake for 20 minutes, flip and bake an additional 15 minutes. Potatoes should be fork-tender.

4. Serve warm or store in the fridge. Use within 5-7 days.

WHOLE

1. Preheat oven to 400 degrees. Wash sweet potatoes and poke holes all over with a fork or knife. Wrap in tin foil or spray with cooking spray and sprinkle with sea salt.

2. Bake for 60 minutes, flipping halfway through.

3. Serve warm or store in a bowl in the fridge. Use within 5-7 days.

ROASTED SPAGHETTI SQUASH

1. Preheat oven to 400 degrees. Cut spaghetti squash into 2-inch rings. Place on a greased baking sheet. Spray the tops of the squash with cooking spray and sprinkle with sea salt. Bake 20 minutes. Flip and bake another 20 minutes.

2. Let cool until you can hold in your hands. Rake squash into a bowl like spaghetti. Serve warm or store in the fridge. Use within 5-7 days.

ROASTED BROCCOLI & BROCCOLINI

1. Preheat oven to 400 degrees. Chop broccoli or broccolini into florets. Place on a baking sheet lined with parchment paper. Spread out into a single layer and spray the tops with cooking spray. Sprinkle with sea salt and other seasonings of choice.

2. Bake 20 minutes. Serve warm or store in the fridge. Use within 5-7 days.

STEAMED GREEN BEANS

1. Bring a ½ inch of salted water to boil in a large frying pan or sauté pan.

2. Add green beans, cover, turn heat down to low and cook until green beans are tender to the bite and water has evaporated, about five minutes (extend the cooking time for softer green beans.)

CASHEW SOUR CREAM

Makes 8 servings / 1 Tbs. per serving
50 calories / 4F / 2C / 1P / per serving

½ cup unsalted cashews
1 Tbs. lemon juice
½ Tbs. olive oil
¼ tsp. sea salt
¼-½ cup water

1. Soak the cashews in water for 30+ minutes.

2. Drain the cashews and add to a high-powered blender. Add the lemon juice, olive oil, sea salt and ¼ cup water.

3. Blend on high. Add an additional ¼ cup water if the mixture is too thick. It should be a pourable consistency, but not too runny. Pour into a sealed container and store in the fridge. Use within 5-7 days.

APPROVED PROTEIN BARS

Built Bars
G2G Bars
Kirkland Protein Bars
No Cow Bars
Oatmega Bars
One Bars Basix Bars (no sucralose)
Perfect Bars
Probar Base Bars
Quest Bars (no sucralose)
RX Bars
Square Bars
Vega Bars

*Visit www.cleansimpleeats.com/blogs/news/bars for our favorite flavors and discount codes!

DAILY SNACKS

SNACK LIKE YOU MEAN IT!

SPICED BANANA ALMOND SHAKE
Makes 1 serving
245 calories / 7F / 27.5C / 18.5P

---

1 cup unsweetened almond milk
¾ serving (24g) CSE Simply Vanilla
   or Cinnamon Roll Protein Powder
½ Tbs. OffBeat Cinnamon Bun Butter
   or natural almond butter
80g frozen banana slices
¼ tsp. almond extract
Dash of cinnamon
Dash of nutmeg
8-10 (130g) ice cubes

1. Add all of the ingredients to a high-powered blender. Blend on high until smooth.

PB PUMPKIN CREAM SHAKE

Makes 1 serving
250 calories / 9F / 26C / 17P

---

1 cup unsweetened almond milk
½ serving (16g) CSE Simply Vanilla or Pumpkin Pie Protein Powder
50g frozen banana slices
¼ cup canned pumpkin
1 Tbs. OffBeat Powdered Peanut Butter
½ Tbs. OffBeat Sweet Classic Peanut Butter
   or natural peanut butter
½ tsp. pumpkin pie spice
8-10 (130g) ice cubes

Topping:
2 Tbs. spray whipped cream

1. Add all of the ingredients to a high-powered blender. Blend on high until smooth.

2. Top with whipped cream and enjoy!

PUMPKIN SPICE SHAKE
Makes 1 serving
240 calories / 7.5F / 24C / 19P

1 cup unsweetened almond milk
¾ serving (24g) CSE Simply Vanilla or Pumpkin Pie Protein Powder
¼ cup canned pumpkin
40g frozen banana slices
½ Tbs. OffBeat Cinnamon Bun Butter, Pumpkin Spice Butter
   or natural almond butter
1 tsp. flaxseed meal
Dash pumpkin pie spice
8-10 (130g) ice cubes

1. Add all of the ingredients to a high-powered blender. Blend on high until smooth.

PEANUT BUTTER COOKIE SHAKE

Makes 1 serving
235 calories / 6.5F / 24.5C / 19P

---

1 cup unsweetened almond milk
½ serving (16g) CSE Simply Vanilla Protein Powder
2 Tbs. old-fashioned rolled oats
30g frozen banana slices
3 Tbs. OffBeat Powdered Peanut Butter
Dash of cinnamon
6-8 (120g) ice cubes

1. Add all of the ingredients to a high-powered blender. Blend on high until smooth.

APPLE CRISP SMOOTHIE
Makes 1 serving
240 calories / 8F / 26C / 16P

¾ cup unsweetened almond milk
75g fresh, chopped apples
¼ cup fat-free cottage cheese
2 Tbs. old-fashioned rolled oats
2 Tbs. (8g) CSE Simply Vanilla Protein Powder
½ Tbs. OffBeat Cinnamon Bun Butter
   or natural almond butter
½ tsp. butter extract
½ tsp. cinnamon
8-10 (130g) ice cubes
Topping:
2 Tbs. spray whipped cream

1. Add all of the ingredients to a high-powered blender. Blend on high until smooth.

2. Top with whipped cream and enjoy!

POST-WORKOUT STRAWBERRY MILK

Makes 1 serving
195 cal / 0F / 20.5C / 30P

---

1 cup cold water
1 ½ servings (48g) CSE Simply Vanilla or Strawberry
   Cheesecake Protein Powder
1 serving CSE Super Berry Mix

1. Add all of the ingredients to a shaker bottle. Shake until smooth.
Enjoy right after your workout.

POST-WORKOUT STRAWBERRY MILKSHAKE

Makes 1 serving
225 cal / 0F / 28C / 28P

---

1 cup fat-free milk
1 serving (32g) CSE Simply Vanilla or Strawberry
   Cheesecake Protein Powder
1 serving CSE Super Berry Mix
¼ tsp. xanthan gum
8-10 (130g) ice cubes

1. Add all of the ingredients to a high-powered blender. Blend on
high until smooth. Enjoy right after your workout.

MILK & COOKIES
Makes 1 serving
245 calories / 7.5F / 25.5C / 19P

½ cup fat-free milk
½ serving (16g) CSE Simply Vanilla Protein Powder
1 serving (32g) CSE Cookie Crumb Granola (recipe on page 67)

1. Add the milk and protien powder to a shaker cup. Shake until smooth.

2. Add the Cookie Crumb Granola to a bowl. Pour milk over the top and enjoy with a spoon.

PUMPKIN PIE PARFAIT
Makes 1 serving
225 calories / 7F / 22C / 18P

⅔ cup plain, nonfat Greek yogurt
2 Tbs. canned pumpkin
Vanilla stevia drops
Dash of cinnamon
Dash of pumpkin pie spice
Toppings:
2 Tbs. Nature's Path Pumpkin Flax Granola
1 Tbs. chopped pecans
1 tsp. raw honey

1. Stir the yogurt, pumpkin, stevia drops, cinnamon and pumpkin pie spice together in a bowl.

2. Top with granola, chopped pecans and a drizzle of raw honey.

SWEET PEAR PARFAIT
Makes 1 serving
230 calories / 5F / 27C / 20P

⅔ cup low-fat cottage cheese
Vanilla stevia drops
Toppings:
80g fresh, chopped pears
1 Tbs. Nature's Path Pumpkin Flax Granola
1 tsp. honey
Dash of cinnamon

1. Mix the cottage cheese together with stevia until you reach your desired sweetness.

2. Top with pears, granola, a drizzle of honey and a dash of cinnamon.

CHOCOLATE COVERED STRAWBERRY PARFAIT
Makes 1 serving
240 calories / 9F / 22C / 18P

½ cup low-fat cottage cheese
Vanilla stevia drops
Toppings:
2 Tbs. Nature's Path Coconut & Cashew Butter Granola
½ cup fresh strawberries
1 Tbs. (14g) OffBeat Midnight Almond Coconut Butter
   or dark chocolate chips

1. Stir cottage cheese and stevia together in a bowl.

2. Top with granola, strawberries, and Midnight Almond Coconut
Butter or melted chocolate chips.

KIWI & POMEGRANATE PARFAIT

Makes 1 serving
235 calories / 7F / 27C / 16P

½ cup plain, nonfat Greek yogurt
Vanilla stevia drops
Toppings:
1 fresh, sliced kiwi
¼ cup pomegranate seeds
1 Tbs. slivered almonds

1. Mix the yogurt and stevia drops together until you reach your desired sweetness.

2. Top with sliced kiwi, pomegranate seeds and almonds.

COOKIE CRUMB GRANOLA PARFAIT

Makes 1 serving
245 calories / 8.5F / 26C / 16.5P

½ cup nonfat, plain Greek yogurt
Vanilla stevia drops
Toppings:
25g sliced bananas or 1 tsp. raw honey
1 serving (32g) CSE Cookie Crumb Granola (recipe on page 67)

1. Mix the yogurt and stevia drops together until you reach your desired sweetness.

2. Top with granola and add the bananas or a drizzle of honey. Enjoy!

COOKIE CRUMB GRANOLA

Makes 24 servings / about 32g per serving
150 calories / 7.5F / 15C / 5P / per serving

½ cup OffBeat Sweet Classic Peanut Butter
   or natural peanut butter
½ cup OffBeat Salted Caramel Butter
   or natural almond butter
½ cup raw honey
½ cup unsweetened flaked coconut
¼ cup flaxseed meal
2 servings CSE Simply Vanilla Protein Powder
2 cups old-fashioned rolled oats
½ tsp. sea salt
½ tsp. vanilla or almond extract

Topping:
¼ cup mini chocolate chips

1. Preheat oven to 350 degrees.

2. Place all the ingredients into a bowl and mix until combined and crumbly.

3. Spread out onto a baking sheet lined with parchment paper. Bake for 5-7 minutes, then flip and bake another 5-7 minutes.

4. Let cool on the cookie sheet for 30 minutes before adding the chocolate chips. Sprinkle the chocolate chips on top (they should melt a little) and pour into an airtight container; store in the fridge.

GREEK ESCAPE
Makes 1 serving
240 calories / 8F / 26C / 16P

---

3 boiled egg whites
3 Tbs. hummus
1 cup veggie of choice
Sea salt
Pepper
Paprika
½ (100g) of a pear

1. Boil three eggs and remove the yolk. Lightly season with salt, pepper and paprika.

2. Use the hummus as a dip for your veggies and eggs. Enjoy the pear on the side.

OPEN-FACED TURKEY & VEGGIE SANDWICH
Makes 1 serving
225 calories / 6F / 26C / 16P

---

2 rice cakes, any variety
2 lettuce leaves
2 red onion slices
2 oz. nitrate-free deli turkey
2 tsp. yellow mustard
4 tomato slices
4 cucumber slices
30g sliced avocado
Dried minced onions
Sea salt and pepper, to taste

1. Layer lettuce, onion, turkey, mustard, tomatoes, cucumbers, and avocado evenly between the two rice cakes. Sprinkle the minced onions, salt and pepper over the top. Enjoy!

APPLES, NUTS, JERKY & GREENS DETOX DRINK

Makes 1 serving
232 calories / 7F / 27C / 15P

1 oz. turkey jerky
65g apple slices
1 Tbs. raw almonds
½ Tbs. pumpkin seeds
Greens Detox Drink:
8 oz. ice cold water
1 serving CSE Super Greens or Peachy Greens Mix
½ of a lemon, juiced
Vanilla stevia drops

1. Arrange all of the snack platter ingredients on a plate.

2. Make the Greens Detox Drink by adding the ice water, CSE Super Greens Mix, lemon juice and stevia to a cup. Mix well and enjoy on the side of the snack platter.

APPLE SLAW & CRACKERS

Makes 1 serving
240 calories / 9F / 24C / 16P

---

2 oz. light chunk tuna, drained
2 Tbs. plain, nonfat Greek yogurt
½ Tbs. olive oil mayo
50g fresh, chopped apples
Splash of lemon juice
Stevia in the Raw, to taste
1 cup coleslaw mix or cabbage
Sea salt and pepper, to taste
12 sweet potato crackers (RW Garcia or Good Thins)

1. Mix the tuna, Greek yogurt, mayo, apples, lemon juice, and stevia together in a bowl. Add coleslaw and salt and pepper to taste. Mix well.

2. Enjoy the crackers on the side, crumble them over the top or scoop the tuna salad up with them.

TURKEY MUFFINS
Makes 2 servings / 2 muffins per serving
220 calories / 8F / 18C / 19P / per serving

6 oz. lean ground turkey
¼ cup shredded mozzarella cheese
¼ minced yellow onions
¼ cup minced red bell peppers
¼ cup old-fashioned rolled oats
¼ cup cooked quinoa (2 Tbs. uncooked)
2 Tbs. tomato paste
1 tsp. Dijon mustard
Splash of apple cider vinegar
Salt and pepper, to taste
Topping:
2 Tbs. Stubb's BBQ Sauce, any variety

1. Preheat oven to 350 degrees.

2. Mix all of the ingredients together with your hands. Grease a muffin tin with cooking spray or use muffin liners. Fill each cup full to the top; should make four.

3. Bake for 30-40 minutes or until the turkey is fully cooked through. Top each serving (two muffins) with one tablespoon of BBQ sauce.

PB TOAST & EGGS
Makes 1 serving
230 calories / 5F / 28C / 17P

---

1 slice Sprouted Grain Ezekiel Bread
½ Tbs. OffBeat Sweet Classic Peanut Butter, Buckeye Brownie
    Peanut Butter, Candy Bar Butter or natural peanut butter
1 large, sliced strawberry
15g banana slices
¼ tsp. chia seeds
1 tsp. raw honey
Dash of cinnamon
Side:
3 egg whites (6 Tbs. liquid egg whites)

1. Toast the bread. Top with nut butter of choice, strawberries, bananas, chia seeds, a drizzle of honey, and a dash of cinnamon.

2. Scramble and season egg whites to your liking and enjoy on the side.

OVER-EASY EGGS & HASH

Makes 1 serving
250 calories / 10F / 23C / 16P

2 large eggs
3 oz. grated sweet potatoes
1 Tbs. minced yellow onions
Sea salt and pepper, to taste
Other seasonings of choice
1 cup veggies of choice

1. Grate sweet potatoes onto a plate. Spray tops with cooking spray and microwave for two minutes. Add to a sauté pan with onions and other veggies of choice. Sauté for two more minutes or until all veggies are tender. Remove from pan.

2. Crack both eggs into the greased pan. Cook two minutes each side, leaving the yolk runny. Lightly season with salt and pepper.

3. Serve the eggs on top of the sweet potato and veggie hash.

MINI QUICHE MUFFINS

Makes 2 servings / 3 muffins per serving
255 calories / 9F / 23C / 22P / per serving

3 large eggs
3 egg whites (6 Tbs. liquid egg whites)
6 oz. grated sweet potatoes
1 slice turkey bacon, chopped
½ cup chopped spinach
2 Tbs. minced yellow onion
2 Tbs. minced red bell peppers
2 chopped mushrooms
Dash garlic powder
Dash onion powder
Dash sea salt
Dash ground black pepper
Topping per serving:
2 Tbs. fresh salsa

1. Preheat oven to 375 degrees.

2. Beat eggs and egg whites together in a large bowl. Add all other ingredients to the bowl and stir until well combined.

3. Prepare six muffin cups by adding liners or greasing each one with cooking spray. Using a ⅓ measuring cup, scoop egg mixture into the muffin tin. Bake for 30 minutes. Top each serving with two tablespoons of salsa.

BROCCOLI, CHEDDAR & BACON OMELET
Makes 1 serving
255 calories / 9F / 22C / 23P

---

1 cup chopped broccoli
1 slice turkey bacon
1 large egg
1 egg white (2 Tbs. liquid egg whites)
Dash granulated garlic
Dash dried minced onion
Sea salt and pepper, to taste
1 tsp. water
1 Tbs. shredded cheddar cheese
Side:
1 slice Sprouted Grain Ezekiel Bread

1. Heat a small frying pan over medium heat. Grease pan and add chopped broccoli and bacon. Cook for about 5 minutes, stirring frequently. Remove from pan.

2. Grease pan again and add egg, egg white, seasonings and a teaspoon of water. Cook for about 5 minutes then flip, carefully. Add bacon, broccoli and cheese to one side of your omelet and flip the other side on top. Cook until cheese is melted.

3. Toast the bread and spray with cooking spray. Enjoy on the side.

PUMPKIN CHOCOLATE CHIP MUG MUFFIN

Makes 1 serving
245 calories / 8.5F / 26C / 18P

---

2 Tbs. unsweetened almond milk
2 Tbs. canned pumpkin
1 large egg
½ tsp. vanilla extract
Stevia, for desired sweetness
⅓ cup CSE Vanilla Pancake & Waffle Mix
5g dark chocolate chips
¼-½ tsp. pumpkin pie spice
Optional Topping:
CSE Maple Syrup

1. Spray a mug or bowl with cooking spray. Whisk milk, pumpkin, egg, vanilla, and stevia together. Stir in the remaining ingredients.

2. Microwave for 60-90 seconds. Enjoy warm, topped with CSE Maple Syrup, if desired (not included in macros).

SPICED WHITE HOT CHOCOLATE
Makes 1 serving
250 calories / 7F / 27.5C / 19P

1 cup fat-free milk
¼ tsp. pumpkin pie spice
¼ tsp. vanilla extract
½ (16g) serving CSE Simply Vanilla or Pumpkin Pie Protein Powder
15g white chocolate chips
Toppings:
4 Tbs. spray whipped cream
Walden Farms caramel syrup, optional garnish

1. In a small pot, combine milk, vanilla extract, and pumpkin pie spice. Whisk over medium-high heat until it begins to simmer. Remove from heat and whisk in the white chocolate chips and protein powder. Stir until completely melted.

2. Pour into a cup and top with whipped cream, a drizzle of caramel syrup and a dusting of pumpkin pie spice.

CHOCOLATE FONDUE POWER DIP

Makes 1 serving
230 calories / 6F / 28C / 16P

140g strawberries
2 Tbs. OffBeat Powdered Peanut Butter
2 Tbs. water
2 Tbs. (8g) CSE Brownie Batter
 or Chocolate Peanut Butter Protein Powder
1 Tbs. OffBeat Buckeye Brownie Peanut Butter
 or 14g melted chocolate chips
1 tsp. raw honey

1. Mix all the ingredients, except the fruit, together in a bowl.

2. Warm in the microwave for 10 seconds and stir. Use as a fondue dip for the fruit of choice. Enjoy!

PUMPKIN CREAM PANCAKES
Makes 1 serving
235 calories / 6F / 25.5C / 20.5P

¼ cup CSE Vanilla Pancake & Waffle Mix
2 Tbs. water
1 large egg
2 Tbs. canned pumpkin
¼ tsp. pumpkin pie spice
Toppings:
¼ cup plain, nonfat Greek yogurt
1 serving Vanilla stevia drops
1 tsp. raw honey
Dash cinnamon

1. Preheat the griddle to medium heat.

2. Whisk the CSE Pancake & Waffle Mix, water, egg, pumpkin, and pumpkin pie spice together in a bowl. Using a ¼ cup measuring cup, pour batter onto the hot griddle. Once small bubbles form on the top, flip and cook on the other side until golden brown.

3. Mix the Greek yogurt and stevia together until you reach your desired sweetness. Spread the sweetened yogurt in between the pancakes. Top with a drizzle of honey and a sprinkle of cinnamon.

APPLE CRUMB MUFFIN & VANILLA SHAKE

Makes 14 muffins / 1 per serving
230 calories / 3F / 27C / 21P / per serving
 *Macros per muffin: 140 calories / 3F / 23.5C / 6P

Shake per serving:
6 oz. cold water
¾ serving (24g) CSE Protein Powder, any flavor
Crumb Topping:
¼ cup CSE Vanilla Pancake & Waffle Mix
¼ cup coconut palm sugar
2 Tbs. melted coconut oil or butter
½ tsp. cinnamon
Pinch of sea salt
Muffins:
½ cup unsweetened almond milk
½ tsp. white wine vinegar
½ cup unsweetened applesauce
½ cup coconut palm sugar
2 large eggs
½ Tbs. vanilla extract
2 cups CSE Vanilla Pancake & Waffle Mix
1 tsp. baking powder
1 tsp. baking soda
1 tsp. cinnamon
½ tsp. sea salt
75g peeled and grated apples

1. Heat oven to 375 degrees. Make the crumb topping first by mixing the CSE Pancake & Waffle Mix, coconut sugar, cinnamon, and sea salt together in a bowl. Stir in the melted coconut oil or butter and store in the fridge.

2. In a small bowl, combine the almond milk and vinegar. Set aside. Beat the applesauce, coconut sugar, and almond milk mixture in a large bowl. Add the eggs and vanilla. Mix until well combined.

3. In a separate bowl, combine the CSE Pancake & Waffle Mix, baking powder, baking soda, cinnamon and sea salt. Mix until well combined. Add the dry ingredients to the wet ingredients and mix until just combined. Fold in the grated apples.

4. Add muffin liners to a muffin tin and spray the liners with cooking spray. Add ¼ cup of the batter to each muffin cup. Sprinkle ½ tablespoon of the crumb mixture over each muffin. Bake in the oven for 14-15 minutes. Enjoy one muffin with the shake listed above.

FALL COOKIE DOUGH BITES

Makes 28 bites
100 calories / 5F / 11C / 4P / per bite

1 cup OffBeat Cinnamon Bun Butter
   or natural almond butter
½ cup raw honey
1 tsp. vanilla extract
1 ½ cups old-fashioned rolled oats
½ tsp. sea salt
½ tsp. ground cinnamon
¼ tsp. ground nutmeg
2 servings CSE Simply Vanilla or Cinnamon Roll Protein Powder

(Easily prepared in a Kitchen Aid Mixer)

1. Place all ingredients into a mixing bowl and stir together until well combined.

2. Scoop into balls using a small cookie scoop. Store in the fridge or freezer. Enjoy!

CARAMEL MACCHIATO BITES

Makes 30 bites
90 calories / 4F / 10.5C / 3P / per bite

1 cup OffBeat Almond Mocha Butter or
   natural almond butter
½ cup raw honey
2 Tbs. Crio Bru grounds or coffee bean grounds
1 serving CSE Caramel Toffee or Simply Vanilla Protein Powder
½ tsp. vanilla extract
Pinch of sea salt
1 ½ cups old-fashioned rolled oats

(Easily prepared in a Kitchen Aid Mixer)

1. Mix all ingredients together, adding the oats last, until well combined.

2. Using a small cookie scoop, scoop into balls and store in the fridge or freezer. Enjoy!

SNICKERS POWER BITES

Makes 28 bites
macros with the cocoa dusting:
    100 calories / 5F / 10.5C / 4P per serving
macros with the chocolate coating:
    110 calories / 5.5F / 11C / 4P / per serving

---

    1 cup OffBeat Candy Bar Peanut Butter, OffBeat Sweet Classic
      Peanut Butter, or natural peanut butter
    ½ cup raw honey
    1 serving CSE Caramel Toffee or Simply Vanilla Protein Powder
    ½ tsp. vanilla extract
    Dash of sea salt
    1 ½ cups old-fashioned rolled oats

Cocoa Dusting
¼ cup cocoa powder

Chocolate Coating
120g dark chocolate chips

(Easily prepared in a Kitchen Aid Mixer)

1. Add all the ingredients to a large bowl and mix until well combined.

2. Using a small cookie scoop, scoop into balls.

3A. If using the Cocoa Dusting method: Add the cocoa powder to a bowl and roll each ball into it. Place in a container and store in the fridge or freezer.

3B. If using the Chocolate Coating method: Add the chocolate chips to a microwave-safe bowl. Microwave in 30 second increments, stirring after each one, until melted and smooth. Place the balls on a baking sheet lined with parchment paper. Drizzle the melted chocolate evenly over each one. Place in the fridge or freezer to allow the chocolate coating to set. Transfer to a container and store in the fridge or freezer. Enjoy!

ALMOND COCONUT BROWNIE BITES
Makes 20 bites
105 calories / 5F / 12C / 3.5P / per bite

½ cup OffBeat Midnight Almond Coconut Butter
  or natural almond butter
½ cup raw honey
2 Tbs. coconut oil
1 tsp. almond extract
6 Tbs. cocoa powder
1 serving CSE Brownie Batter or Coconut Cream Protein Powder
¼ cup unsweetened finely shredded coconut
1 cup oat flour

(Easily prepared in a Kitchen Aid Mixer)

1. Mix almond butter, honey, coconut oil, almond extract, cocoa powder and protein powder in a bowl. Add oat flour and mix well.

2. Chill in the fridge for at least 30 minutes. Using a small cookie scoop, scoop into balls and roll in shredded coconut. Store in the fridge or freezer. Enjoy!

PUMPKIN PIE ENERGY BITES

Makes 32 bites
85 calories / 4F / 9C / 3P / per bite

1⅓ cups Medjool dates, pitted
1 cup pecans
½ cup unsweetened shredded coconut
½ cup canned pumpkin
1 Tbs. vanilla extract
2 tsp. ground cinnamon
½ tsp. ground nutmeg
Dash of ground cloves
Dash of sea salt
2 servings CSE Simply Vanilla or Pumpkin Pie Protein Powder
2 cups old-fashioned rolled oats

(Easily prepared in a Kitchen Aid Mixer)

1. Soak dates for 10 minutes. Drain.

2. Place pecans in a food processor or high-powered blender and pulse until broken up. Add the dates, coconut, pumpkin, vanilla, spices and salt. Pulse until combined.

3. Transfer to a bowl and stir in protein powder and oats. Store in the fridge for 30 minutes. Using a cookie scoop, roll into balls and store in the fridge or freezer. Enjoy!

COCONUT CASHEW MACAROON BITES

Makes 35 bites
90 calories / 4.5F / 10C / 3P / per bite

---

1 cup OffBeat Aloha Butter or
   Toasted Coconut Cashew Butter (recipe below)
½ cup raw honey
2 servings CSE Simply Vanilla or Coconut Cream Protein Powder
½ cup unsweetened coconut flakes
1 tsp. vanilla extract
Pinch of sea salt
2 cups old-fashioned rolled oats

(Easily prepared in a Kitchen Aid Mixer)

1. Mix all ingredients together, adding the oats last, until well combined.

2. Using a small cookie scoop, scoop into balls and store in the fridge or freezer. Enjoy!

TOASTED COCONUT CASHEW BUTTER

Makes 1 cup / 16 servings
100 calories / 8.5F / 5C / 3P / per Tbs.

280g roasted, salted cashews
60g unsweetened coconut flakes

1. Place cashews and coconut into a blender and blend until smooth, scraping down the sides in between blends if needed. Pour into a jar or container and store in the fridge.

FIRST BREAKFAST, THEN EVERYTHING ELSE

ALMOND JOY PROTEIN SHAKE

Makes 1 serving
345 calories / 11.5F / 34.5C / 25.5P

---

1 cup unsweetened almond milk
1 serving CSE Brownie Batter Protein Powder
2 Tbs. old-fashioned rolled oats
60g frozen banana slices
1 Tbs. cocoa powder
1 Tbs. unsweetened shredded coconut
½ Tbs. OffBeat Midnight Almond Coconut Butter
   or natural almond butter
½ tsp. vanilla extract
½ tsp. coconut extract
6-8 (120g) ice cubes

1. Add all of the ingredients to a high-powered blender. Blend until smooth. Enjoy!

APPLE CINNAMON PROTEIN PANCAKES

Makes 4 servings
350 calories / 11F / 36.5C / 25.5P / per serving

1 ¼ cups CSE Vanilla Pancake & Waffle Mix
1 serving CSE Simply Vanilla
   or Snickerdoodle Protein Powder
1 tsp. cinnamon
½ tsp. nutmeg
¾ cup unsweetened almond milk
2 large eggs
¼ cup liquid egg whites
40g mashed banana
2 tsp. vanilla extract
1 cup grated apples
½ cup chopped pecans
Toppings per serving:
3 Tbs. nonfat, plain Greek yogurt
8 Tbs. liquid CSE Maple Syrup

1. Preheat the griddle to medium heat.

2. Mix the CSE Pancake & Waffle Mix, protein powder, cinnamon and nutmeg together in a bowl; set aside.

3. In a separate bowl, whisk the milk, eggs, egg whites, banana and vanilla together. Add the wet mixture to the dry, and stir until just combined.

4. Grate apples. Squeeze as much moisture as you can out of them with your hands, and then fold them into the pancake batter along with the pecans.

5. Spray the griddle with cooking spray. Using a ¼ measuring cup, pour the batter onto the griddle. Once bubbles form on the top, flip and cook on the other side until golden brown. Weigh all the pancakes and divide the weight by four to get the amount needed to fill one serving.

6. Mix the Greek yogurt and syrup together in a bowl. Weigh the mixture and divide it by four to get the amount needed to fill one serving. Drizzle one serving of the creamy syrup over one serving of the pancakes.

PUMPKIN PIE OVERNIGHT OATS

Makes 2 servings
350 calories / 12F / 35.5C / 25P / per serving

¾ cup old-fashioned rolled oats
1 cup unsweetened almond milk
¼ cup nonfat, plain Greek yogurt
¼ cup canned pumpkin
1 ½ Tbs. OffBeat Pumpkin Spice, Cinnamon Bun Butter
   or natural almond butter
1 ½ servings CSE Pumpkin Pie or Simply Vanilla Protein Powder
1 tsp. pumpkin pie spice
Toppings per serving (add just before eating):
2 Tbs. spray whipped cream
1 tsp. chopped pecans

1. Stir all ingredients together in a large bowl. Weigh the mixture and divide the weight by two to get the amount needed to fill one serving. Evenly distribute into two jars or containers. Cover and store in the fridge overnight.

2. Enjoy cold topped with whipped cream and chopped pecans. Stores well in the fridge for up to five days.

*Multiply the recipe by five to make ten servings that will last you all week!

BREAKFAST BURRITOS

Makes 4 servings
340 calories / 11F / 34C / 26P / per serving

4 Sugarhouse Maple Chicken Sausages
4 oz. grated red potatoes
½ cup green bell peppers
2 cups chopped spinach
½ cup diced yellow onions
Dash garlic powder
Dash onion powder
Dash sea salt and pepper, to taste
4 large eggs
8 egg whites (1 cup liquid egg whites)
4 whole grain tortillas (120 calories each)
½ cup low-fat, shredded mozzarella cheese
Toppings per serving:
2 Tbs. salsa

1. Heat a skillet to medium heat.

2. Chop chicken sausage and add to the skillet with the grated potatoes, chopped peppers, spinach and diced onions. Sauté until veggies are tender and sausage is browned. Add the eggs, egg whites and seasonings. Cook until eggs are cooked through. Weigh the mixture and divide by four to get the amount needed to fill one serving.

3. Lay out the tortillas and fill them evenly with ¼ of the mixture and two tablespoons of mozzarella cheese. Roll the tortillas up tight and enjoy warm dipped in salsa. Wrap the extras in foil and store in the fridge or freezer until ready to eat.

*Spray the foil with nonstick cooking spray when wrapping up the burritos to avoid tortillas from sticking.

*To reheat from the fridge, place in the oven at 400 degrees for 30 minutes; 50-60 minutes if frozen.

HOT APPLE PIE OATS

Makes 1 serving
330 calories / 11F / 34C / 26P

⅓ cup old-fashioned rolled oats
½ cup water
¼ cup liquid egg whites
60g fresh, chopped apples
2 tsp. OffBeat Cinnamon Bun Butter
   or natural almond butter
1 tsp. grass-fed butter
Dash cinnamon
Dash nutmeg
½ serving (16g) CSE Simply Vanilla
   or Cinnamon Roll Protein Powder

Topping:
2 Tbs. nonfat, plain Greek yogurt
Vanilla stevia drops

1. Stir raw oats, water, egg whites and apples together in a bowl. Mix well and microwave for 1-2 minutes. Stir in nut butter, butter, cinnamon and nutmeg. Stir in protein powder last.

2. Stir Greek yogurt and stevia together in a bowl. Top oatmeal with yogurt and enjoy warm.

PUMPKIN PROTEIN WAFFLES

Makes 4 servings
350 calories / 12F / 34.5C / 25.5P / per serving

---

1 cup CSE Vanilla Pancake & Waffle Mix
2 servings (64g) CSE Pumpkin Pie or Simply Vanilla Protein Powder
½ cup canned pumpkin
½ cup unsweetened almond milk
2 large eggs
2 tsp. pumpkin pie spice
Toppings per serving:
1 Tbs. OffBeat Pumpkin Spice, Salted Caramel Butter
   or natural almond butter
1 Tbs. liquid CSE Maple Syrup
2 Tbs. spray whipped cream

1. Heat waffle iron.

2. Add the CSE Pancake & Waffle Mix, protein powder, pumpkin, almond milk, eggs, and pumpkin pie spice to a high-powered blender. Blend until smooth.

3. Pour into the waffle iron and cook for two minutes (these burn easily, so watch closely). Remove from the waffle iron and weigh the waffles, then divide into four servings.

4. Make the CSE Maple Syrup Mix by mixing with water. Drizzle the nut butter and syrup over the waffles and then top with whipped cream.

SUPERFOOD CEREAL

Makes 1 serving
340 calories / 11F / 35C / 24.5P

¾ cup unsweetened almond milk
½ serving CSE Simply Vanilla Protein Powder
¾ cup Kashi GO Original Cereal
2 Tbs. fresh blueberries
2 Tbs. sliced almonds
1 tsp. chia seeds
Dash of cinnamon

1. Add the cereal, protein powder, almonds, chia seeds and cinnamon to a bowl. Stir until well combined.

2. Pour the milk over the cereal and top with blueberries. Enjoy!

BACON, EGG & AVOCADO SANDWICH

Makes 1 serving
335 calories / 11F / 35C / 24P

---

1 multigrain English muffin
1 large egg
2 egg whites (¼ cup liquid egg whites)
Sea salt and pepper, to taste
1 slice turkey bacon
½ cup Spring Mix Greens
2 tomato slices
25g sliced avocado

1. Heat a skillet to medium-high heat.

2. Fry the eggs and season to your liking. Remove from pan and cook the turkey bacon until crispy.

3. Toast the muffin.

4. Sandwich the greens, bacon, eggs, tomato and avocado in the middle. Enjoy warm.

DOUBLE CHOCOLATE PB OATMEAL

Makes 1 serving
355 calories / 13F / 35C / 27P

⅓ cup old-fashioned rolled oats
½ cup water
3 Tbs. (46g) liquid egg whites
1 Tbs. OffBeat Powdered Peanut Butter
½ Tbs. OffBeat Sweet Classic Peanut Butter
   or Buckeye Brownie Peanut Butter
   or natural peanut butter
½ serving (17g) CSE Brownie Batter
   or Chocolate Peanut Butter Protein Powder
20g sliced banana
1 Tbs. OffBeat Buckeye Brownie Peanut Butter
   or 14g dark chocolate chips

1. Add the rolled oats, water, egg whites and powdered peanut butter to a bowl. Mix well and microwave on high for 1½ minutes.

2. Stir in the peanut butter and let cool a bit. Stir in protein powder until well combined.

3. Add the sliced bananas.

4. Melt the OffBeat Buckeye Brownie Peanut Butter or chocolate chips and drizzle over the top. Enjoy!

APPLE BUTTER CREPES

Makes 4 servings
350 calories / 12F / 36C / 24.5P / per serving

---

2 large eggs
6 egg whites (¾ cup liquid egg whites)
1 (100g) banana
1 cup CSE Vanilla Pancake & Waffle Mix
½ cup unsweetened almond milk
2 tsp. cinnamon
1 tsp. stevia

Crepe filling and topping:
1 (150g) apple
½ Tbs. coconut oil
1 tsp. cinnamon
¼ cup OffBeat Cinnamon Bun, Salted Caramel Butter or
   natural almond butter
½ serving CSE Simply Vanilla or Snickerdoodle Protein Powder
½ cup nonfat, plain Greek yogurt
4 Tbs. liquid CSE Maple Syrup

1. Heat a large frying pan over medium heat. Chop the apples.

2. Add all the crepe ingredients to a blender and blend until smooth.

3. Spray the pan with cooking spray and pour ½ cup of the mixture into the pan. Swirl the pan around to make a thin crepe. Wait until it bubbles, then flip carefully and cook for 30 more seconds on the other side. Repeat with remaining batter. Weigh all the crepes and divide the weight by four to get the amount needed to fill one serving.

4. Add the apples, coconut oil and cinnamon in the frying pan. Sauté over medium heat until tender and fragrant. Remove from heat.

5. Mix the nut butter, protein powder and Greek yogurt together in a bowl. Weigh the mixture and divide the weight by four equal portions. Spread one serving of the filling into one serving of crepes. Top with ¼ of the warm apples and roll up. Drizzle with one tablespoon of syrup. Enjoy!

PUMPKIN FRENCH TOAST

Makes 4 servings
345 calories / 11F / 36C / 24P / per serving

½ cup canned pumpkin
¼ cup unsweetened almond milk
4 large eggs
1 tsp. vanilla
1 tsp. pumpkin pie spice
8 slices Sprouted Grain Ezekiel Bread
Topping per serving:
¼ cup low-fat cottage cheese
Vanilla stevia drops, to taste
1 Tbs. chopped pecans
Dash cinnamon
CSE Maple Syrup, optional

1. Heat griddle to medium heat.

2. Whisk the pumpkin, almond milk, eggs, vanilla and pumpkin pie spice together in an 8x8 baking pan. Dip the bread into the mixture and let sit for a minute to soak up the goodness. Place on the greased griddle. Once lightly browned, flip and cook until lightly browned on the other side.

3. Mix the cottage cheese with stevia to sweeten. Top each two slices of French toast with ¼ cup cottage cheese, one tablespoon of chopped pecans, syrup and a dash of cinnamon. Top with CSE Maple Syrup, if desired (not included in macros).

ONE PAN COUNTRY SKILLET

Makes 4 servings
330 calories / 11F / 32C / 26P / per serving

---

12 oz. lean ground turkey
24 oz. diced red potatoes or sweet potatoes
2 cups chopped spinach
1 cup chopped yellow onions
1 cup chopped mushrooms
Dash onion powder
Dash garlic powder
Dash sea salt and pepper, to taste
Toppings per serving:
1 large egg
2 Tbs. salsa

1. Place diced potatoes on a plate, spray tops with cooking spray and microwave for two minutes.

2. Heat a skillet to medium heat. Spray with cooking spray, then add the ground turkey. Cook until cooked through and browned. Add the potatoes, spinach, onions, mushrooms and seasonings. Cook for three minutes or until the onions are soft. Remove from pan and weigh the mixture. Divide by four to get the amount needed to fill one serving.

3. Spray the pan and fry the eggs to your liking. Season with sea salt and pepper. Place on top of the turkey and veggies. Enjoy with salsa.

CINNA-BERRY BREAKFAST SQUARES

Makes 12 servings
345 calories / 12F / 34.5C / 24.5P / per serving

---

2 ½ cups old-fashioned rolled oats
½ cup chopped pecans
1 Tbs. cinnamon
1 tsp. baking powder
½ tsp. sea salt
2 cups unsweetened almond milk
2 servings CSE Simply Vanilla or Cinnamon Roll Protein Powder
2 large eggs
½ cup raw honey
2 Tbs. unsweetened applesauce
2 tsp. vanilla extract
2 (240g) bananas
1 cup blueberries
½ cup blackberries
Topping per serving:
2 Tbs. spray whipped cream
Side per serving:
1 large egg
3 egg whites (6 Tbs. liquid egg whites)

1. Preheat oven to 375 degrees.

2. In a large bowl, stir the oats, pecans, cinnamon, baking powder and salt together. Set aside.

3. In a separate bowl beat the almond milk, protein powder, two eggs, honey, applesauce and vanilla together. Set aside.

4. Grease a 9x13 baking dish. Slice the bananas and place them in a single layer on the bottom of the pan. Layer the blueberries, the dry oat mixture, the wet mixture over the dry and then top with the blackberries. Bake for 40 minutes.

5. Enjoy warm topped with whipped cream.

6. Cook the eggs to your liking and enjoy on the side.

LEMON RASPBERRY FLOURLESS CREPES

Makes 4 servings
340 calories / 12.5F / 32C / 25P / per serving

4 large eggs
12 egg whites (1½ cups liquid egg whites)
200g bananas
1 serving CSE Simply Vanilla Protein Powder
Toppings per serving:
3 oz. Lemon Noosa Yoghurt
    or 1 Tbs. OffBeat Lemon Coconut Bliss Butter
½ cup fresh raspberries
1 tsp. raw honey

1. Heat a large frying pan over medium heat.

2. Add the eggs, egg whites, bananas and protein powder to a blender. Blend on high until well combined. Batter will be really thin.

3. Grease the pan well and pour ¼ cup of the mixture into the pan. Twirl the batter around until the pan is coated and the crepe is thin. Once the edges begin to brown and pull away from the sides of the pan, flip carefully. Cook for 30-60 seconds and transfer to a plate. Should make 12 crepes; three per serving.

4. Divide 3 oz. lemon yoghurt or one tablespoon of the Lemon Coconut Bliss Buttter, and ½ cup fresh raspberries between three crepes. Drizzle butter or yoghurt in the centers, then add the fresh raspberries. Roll or fold up and then drizzle honey over the top.

ENTREES

GOOD FOOD

=

GOOD MOOD

AUTUMN SALAD SANDWICH

Makes 2 servings
345 calories / 12F / 34C / 25P / per serving

2 slices Ezekiel bread
3 oz. cooked and shredded chicken breast (4 oz. raw)
2 cups chopped baby kale
100g chopped apples
2 Tbs. chopped cashews
2 Tbs. olive oil mayo
2 Tbs. nonfat, plain Greek yogurt
1 tsp. apple cider vinegar
Dash of stevia
Dash of salt
Dash of pepper

1. Mix all of the salad ingredients together in a large bowl.

2. Toast the Ezekiel bread and then pile ½ of the mixture on top of each slice. One slice per serving. Enjoy!

CHICKEN ENCHILADA STUFFED SPAGHETTI SQUASH

Makes 4 servings
350 calories / 12F / 33C / 28P / per serving

---

4 cups cooked spaghetti squash
8 oz. cooked and shredded chicken breast (12 oz. raw)
4 oz. canned, chopped green chiles
4 lite Laughing Cow cheese wedges
½ cup black beans, drained
1 cup red or green enchilada sauce
½ cup lowfat, shredded mozzarella cheese
120g avocado
Green onions, for garnish
Side per serving:
75g sliced apples or pears

1. Heat oven to 425 degrees. Cut each spaghetti squash in half lengthwise and spoon out the seeds. Sprinkle the inside with sea salt and then place face down on a baking sheet lined with parchment paper. Bake for 40-45 minutes or until tender. Let cool.

2. Cook and shred the chicken according to the directions in the Food Prep Guide.

3. Combine the shredded chicken, green chiles, cheese wedges and black beans together in a bowl.

4. Rake the cooked spaghetti squash into a large bowl with a fork. Place one cup of the spaghetti squash back into each shell, then add ¼ of the chicken mixture to each one. Top each serving with ¼ cup enchilada sauce and two tablespoons of shredded cheese.

5. Turn oven down to 350 degrees. Return stuffed spaghetti squash back to the oven and bake another 10 minutes or until the cheese is melted and the chicken mixture is heated through. Top each serving with 30g chopped avocado, green onions, salt and pepper to taste. Enjoy fruit on the side.

TACO SOUP

Makes 4 servings
340 calories / 12F / 33C / 26P / per serving

8 oz. lean ground turkey
½ cup chopped yellow onion
2 cups crushed tomatoes
1 cup frozen yellow corn
1 cup black beans or kidney beans
2 Tbs. taco seasoning
Toppings per serving:
2 Tbs. mozzarella cheese
1 Tbs. nonfat, plain Greek yogurt
25g avocado
Sea salt and pepper

1. In a large soup pot, brown the ground turkey with the chopped yellow onion over medium-high heat. Once browned, add the crushed tomatoes, corn, beans and taco seasoning. Let simmer for 30 minutes.

2. Weigh the entire recipe and divide the weight by four to get the amount needed to fill one serving. Top each serving with two tablespoons of shredded mozzarella cheese, one tablespoon of plain Greek yogurt, 25g avocado, salt and pepper to taste.

HARVEST COBB SALAD

Makes 4 servings
350 calories / 14F / 30C / 25P / per serving

---

4 oz. grilled chicken breast (6 oz. raw)
4 hard-boiled eggs, sliced
4 cups cubed and roasted butternut squash
4 slices turkey bacon
8 cups chopped spinach
4 Tbs. chopped pecans
Sea salt and pepper, to taste

Honey Mustard Dressing:
½ cup low-fat mayo
2 Tbs. lemon juice
2 Tbs. raw honey
2 Tbs. Dijon mustard
1 tsp. dry mustard

1. Grill the chicken breast and boil the eggs according to the directions in the Food Prep Guide. Cook the bacon until crispy.

2. Place butternut squash in a single layer on a large baking sheet lined with parchment paper. Spray the tops with cooking spray and sprinkle with sea salt. Roast for 50-60 minutes, flipping halfway.

3. For one serving, layer two cups of spinach, one hard-boiled egg, 1 oz. grilled chicken breast, one slice cooked and chopped bacon, one cup roasted butternut squash and one tablespoon chopped pecans.

4. Blend all the dressing ingredients together in a blender until smooth. Weigh the dressing and divide the weight by four to get the amount needed to fill one serving. Drizzle one portion over deach salad. Top with sea salt and ground black pepper.

PARMESAN CRUSTED SALMON

Makes 4 servings
335 calories / 11F / 32C / 27P / per serving

---

2 cups cooked quinoa (1 cup uncooked)
4 cups broccoli florets
Dash garlic powder
Dash onion powder
12 oz. wild caught salmon
2 Tbs. plain, nonfat Greek yogurt
1 Tbs. fresh lemon juice
1 tsp. minced garlic
½ tsp. sea salt
Dash black pepper
¼ cup finely grated Parmesan cheese
¼ cup whole grain bread crumbs
Pinch of flat-leaf parsley
1 tsp. lemon zest
Dash of thyme
1 Tbs. olive oil

1. Preheat oven to 400 degrees. Cook quinoa according to directions on package.

2. Chop broccoli into florets and place on a baking sheet lined with parchment paper. Spray the tops with cooking spray and sprinkle with onion powder, garlic powder and sea salt. Bake broccoli for five minutes then remove from the oven. Sprinkle bottoms of salmon with sea salt and place on the same baking sheet.

3. Mix the Greek yogurt, lemon juice and garlic together in a bowl. Spread evenly onto the salmon fillets.

4. Combine the Parmesan cheese, bread crumbs, parsley, lemon zest, thyme and olive oil together in a separate bowl. Evenly press over the tops of the salmon. Bake for 15 minutes or until the salmon is fully cooked through and the broccoli is lightly browned. Divide into four equal portions. Serve each portion with ½ cup cooked quinoa on the side.

PEPPERONI PIZZA PINWHEELS

Makes 4 servings
335 calories / 12.5F / 32C / 26.5P / per serving

¾ cup white whole wheat flour
1 tsp. baking powder
¼ tsp. sea salt
Dash garlic powder
Dash onion powder
4 Tbs. nutritional yeast flakes
½ cup plain, nonfat Greek yogurt
½ cup traditional marinara sauce
2 oz. turkey pepperoni
1 ¼ cups mozzarella cheese, shredded
4 cups broccoli
1 Tbs. olive oil
Sea salt

1. Preheat oven to 425 degrees.

2. Whisk the flour, baking powder, sea salt, garlic powder, onion powder, and three tablespoons of nutritional yeast flakes together in a bowl. Add the Greek yogurt and use a rubber spatula to fold it in until well combined. If the dough is too dry, add a tiny bit of water; if it's too sticky, flour the surface before rolling out.

3. Roll the dough out into a large rectangular shape. Spread the marinara sauce evenly over the dough, add the pepperoni and cheese. Carefully roll the dough up lengthwise and slice into eight equal pinwheels. Place on a greased baking sheet or muffin tin. Bake for 12-15 minutes. Two pinwheels per serving.

4. Chop the broccoli into florets and place on a baking sheet lined with parchment paper. Drizzle the olive oil over the top, then spray with cooking spray. Sprinkle with sea salt and one tablespoon of nutritional yeast (this will give it a cheesy flavor and added nutritional value). Bake for 15-20 minutes. Enjoy on the side of your pinwheels.

BBQ BEEF SANDWICH & SLAW

Makes 4 servings
350 calories / 10F / 38C / 27P / per serving

---

8 oz. lean beef brisket or roast
¼ cup Stubb's BBQ sauce, any variety
¼ cup water
2 cups coleslaw mix (without dressing)
¼ cup chopped red onion
2 Tbs. plain, nonfat Greek yogurt
2 Tbs. olive oil mayo
2 tsp. lemon juice
2 tsp. apple cider vinegar
Dash sea salt
Dash pepper
Dash celery seed
Stevia, for added sweetness
4 Ezekiel English muffins

1. Place the roast in a crockpot or slow cooker. Cover halfway with water. Cook on low for 4 hours. Remove the roast, dump out the water and clean out the crockpot. Place the roast back in with the BBQ sauce and ¼ cup of water. Cook an additional 2-4 hours on low or until cooked through.

2. Make the coleslaw by combining the coleslaw mix, red onion, yogurt, mayo, lemon juice, vinegar, sea salt, pepper, celery seed and stevia. Store covered in the fridge until ready to use.

3. Shred the beef brisket with forks and stir until well combined with BBQ sauce. Lean brisket or roast can be tough to shred. If unable to shred easily, slice into equal portions.

4. Toast the English muffins. Sandwich ¼ of the BBQ beef and ¼ of the coleslaw in between each muffin. Enjoy warm.

CHICKEN FETTUCCINE ALFREDO

Makes 4 servings
360 calories / 12F / 35C / 28P / per serving

6 oz. grilled chicken breast (8 oz. raw)
5 oz. dry whole wheat fettuccine
2 cups cauliflower florets
Sea salt, dash
½ cup unsweetened almond milk
1 Tbs. olive oil
1 Tbs. grass-fed butter
12 cherry tomatoes, halved
2 cloves garlic, chopped
Black pepper
¼ cup grated Parmesan cheese
2 Tbs. nutritional yeast flakes
½ cup marinara sauce
⅓ cup low-fat, shredded mozzarella cheese
Fresh basil

1. Cook the chicken according to the directions in the Food Prep Guide. Cook the fettucine according to the directions on the package.

2. Bring a large pot of water to a boil. Add the cauliflower and sea salt. Boil until cauliflower is tender; about 10 minutes. Drain. Place in a blender with the almond milk; blend until smooth.

3. Add the olive oil, butter and tomatoes to a large pot. Cook over medium-low heat until the butter is melted. Add the garlic, black pepper and the creamed cauliflower. Bring mixture to a simmer, stirring constantly. Add the Parmesan cheese, nutritional yeast, and marinara sauce to the pot and simmer for 8-10 minutes. Stir in the mozzarella cheese until smooth. Remove from heat.

4. Add the pasta to the sauce. Weigh the pasta with the sauce and divide the weight by four to get the amount needed to fill one serving. Top each serving with 1.5 oz. grilled chicken breast and fresh basil. Season with sea salt and pepper to taste.

HONEY GARLIC CHICKEN TACOS

Makes 4 servings
340 calories / 10F / 35C / 27P / per serving

---

2 Tbs. raw honey
1 ½ Tbs. taco seasoning
3 cloves garlic, minced
1 Tbs. melted coconut oil
¼ tsp. sea salt
14 oz. raw chicken breasts (10.5 oz. cooked)
8 corn tortillas (6-inch)
1 cup chopped green cabbage
4 Tbs. Cashew Sour Cream (recipe in Food Prep Guide)
4 Tbs. salsa
1 lime, cut into wedges
Green onions, for garnish
Cilantro, for garnish

1. Spray a crockpot with cooking spray and heat on low.

2. In a large bowl, mix the honey, taco seasoning, garlic, melted coconut oil and sea salt. Add the chicken to the bowl and toss to coat. Add the chicken to the crockpot and pour the remaining mixture over the top. Cook on low heat for three hours. Shred the chicken and let cook another 2-3 hours.

3. Weigh the chicken and divide by four to get the amount needed to fill one serving. Evenly distribute the chicken mixture into the corn tortillas. Top each one with cabbage, ½ tablespoon of cashew sour cream, ½ tablespoon of salsa, lime juice, green onions and cilantro. Enjoy two tacos per serving.

OPEN-FACED TUNA MELT

Makes 4 servings
345 calories / 11F / 37C / 24.5P / per serving

10 oz. canned chunk light tuna (weigh after drained)
1 shallot, minced
2 Tbs. olive oil mayo
1 Tbs. fresh lemon juice
1 Tbs. minced flat-leaf parsley
1 tsp. Sriracha sauce
4 multigrain English muffins
8 tomato slices
¾ cup low-fat, shredded cheddar cheese
8 celery sticks
Topping per serving:
15g sliced avocado
Black pepper
Sea salt

1. Preheat oven to high broil.

2. Combine the tuna, shallots, mayo, lemon juice, parsley and Sriracha sauce in a small bowl. Weigh the mixture and divide by four to get the amount needed to fill one serving. Evenly distribute the mixture on top of each muffin, leaving it open-faced. Top each muffin half with one tomato slice and 1 ½ tablespoons of shredded cheddar cheese.

3. Place muffins on a baking sheet and broil for 3-5 minutes or until the cheese is melted and lightly browned. Two muffin halves per serving. Divide the 15g avocado between the two muffin halves then add salt and pepper to taste. Enjoy warm with 2 celery sticks on the side.

GRILLED CHEESE & TOMATO BASIL SOUP

Makes 4 servings

340 calories / 12.5F / 32C / 25P / per serving

Tomato Soup:
1 Tbs. olive oil
1 tsp. minced garlic
1 celery stick, sliced
2 small (6 oz.) carrots, peeled and chopped
½ cup diced yellow onions
Sea salt and pepper, to taste
A pinch of fresh basil or ¼ tsp. dried basil
28 oz. fire roasted diced tomatoes, canned
1 tsp. Stevia in the Raw
1 cup chicken bone broth
2 bay leaves
1 Tbs. grass-fed butter
½ cup light coconut milk, canned
Grilled Turkey & Cheese:
4 slices Sprouted Grain Ezekiel Bread
10 oz. nitrate-free deli turkey
½ cup low-fat, shredded mozzarella cheese
Handful of chopped spinach

1. Heat a large pot over medium heat. Add olive oil, garlic, celery, carrots, onions and basil. Sprinkle in some salt and pepper. Sauté until veggies are tender. Add the diced tomatoes and stevia and stir. Add the bone broth, bay leaves and butter. Return to a simmer until the veggies are really soft, about 15-20 minutes. Add the coconut milk. Stir until well combined. Remove the bay leaves.

2. Transfer soup to a high-powered blender and blend until smooth. Make sure the lid is on tight and the blender is not too full; blend in a couple different batches if necessary.

3. Make the grilled cheese sandwiches by placing 5 oz. of turkey, ¼ cup of cheese and some spinach in between each two slices of bread. Cook in a panini press, sandwich maker, or in a covered frying a pan over medium heat. Cook until the cheese is melted and the bread is toasted. Slice each sandwich in half; one half sandwich per serving.

4. Weigh the entire soup recipe and divide the weight by four to get the amount needed to fill one serving. Enjoy the grilled cheese on the side or dip in the soup.

THAI CHICKEN PIZZA

Makes 4 servings
350 calories / 15F / 29C / 25P / per serving

---

1 ½ cups CSE Buttermilk Pancake & Waffle Mix
2 Tbs. olive oil
6 Tbs. hot water
½ cup low-fat, shredded mozzarella cheese
4 oz. grilled chicken breast (5.5 oz. raw)
2 oz. matchstick carrots
¼ cup chopped red onions
2 cups chopped spinach
Green onions, for garnish
Cilantro, for garnish

Thai Peanut Sauce:
1 Tbs. OffBeat Sweet Classic Peanut Butter
  or natural peanut butter
4 Tbs. salsa
1 tsp. raw honey
1 tsp. coconut aminos or low-sodium soy sauce

1. Preheat oven to 450 degrees.

2. Combine the CSE Pancake & Waffle Mix, olive oil and hot water together. Knead with hands until well combined. If it's too dry, add a little more water. Place on a baking sheet lined with parchment paper and roll out into a thin circle. Should roll out easily without crumbling. Bake crust for 8 minutes.

3. Blend the peanut butter, salsa, honey and coconut aminos in a blender until smooth. Spread the Thai Peanut Sauce evenly over the dough. Top with cheese, grilled chicken, carrots, red onions and chopped spinach.

4. Bake for 10 minutes or until the cheese is melted and the veggies are tender. Garnish with green onions and cilantro and slice into four servings. Enjoy warm.

TURKEY POT PIES

Makes 4 servings

330 calories / 13.5F / 32C / 25P / per serving

Filling:
½ cup chopped carrots
½ cup thinly sliced celery
¼ cup finely chopped yellow onion
2 Tbs. CSE Buttermilk Pancake & Waffle Mix
Dash of sea salt
Dash of black pepper
¾ cup low-sodium chicken broth
¼ cup unsweetened almond milk
½ cup frozen peas
8 oz. chopped, roasted turkey breast
Crust:
1 ½ cups CSE Buttermilk Pancake & Waffle Mix
1 Tbs. grass-fed butter
2 Tbs. olive oil
3-4 Tbs. ice water

1. Preheat oven to 425 degrees.

2. Spray a small sauce pan with cooking spray and add carrots, celery and onions. Sauté on medium-high heat until onions are translucent. Turn down heat and add two tablespoons of CSE Pancake & Waffle Mix, salt and pepper. Mix well.

3. Slowly stir in the chicken broth and milk. Bring to a boil and then turn down to low and let simmer about five minutes or until sauce begins to thicken. Stir in the peas and turkey. Mix well and set aside.

4. For the crust, pour the CSE Pancake & Waffle Mix into a bowl. Cut butter into the mix with two knives until butter is in very small pieces. Add the olive oil, then slowly add the ice water until the dough comes together and isn't sticky. You may not need all the water.

5. Roll out the dough into a rectangle between two sheets of parchment paper. Dough should be thin, about ⅛ of an inch, as it will puff when it bakes. Peel the top piece of parchment paper off dough and slice into eight equal portions. Place four pieces of the dough face down into four mini pie dishes. Press the dough to fit the dish and create a crust edge.

6. Evenly pour ¼ of the turkey mixture into each pie dish and cover with the top crust, pinching the edges together. Place the mini pie dishes on a baking sheet. Cut a couple slits in the top of each pie and bake for 20 minutes. Enjoy warm.

THAI PEANUT SPAGHETTI

Makes 4 servings
350 calories / 11F / 36C / 27P / per serving

---

4 oz. dry whole grain spaghetti
9 oz. grilled chicken breast (12 oz. raw)
1 cup shredded green cabbage
1 cup matchstick carrots
2 shallots, sliced
½ oz. chopped peanuts
Green onions, for garnish

Thai Sauce:

½ cup salsa
¼ cup OffBeat Sweet Classic Peanut Butter
   or natural peanut butter
1 Tbs. coconut aminos or low-sodium soy sauce
1 Tbs. raw honey

1. Cook the spaghetti according to the directions on the package.

2. Add all the sauce ingredients to a blender or food processor and blend until smooth. Set aside.

3. Heat a skillet to medium heat. Spray with cooking spray and add the chopped, raw chicken. Stir until fully cooked through. Add the cabbage, carrots and shallots. Sauté for 3-5 minutes or until the veggies are tender-crisp.

4. Turn the heat down to low, then add the cooked spaghetti and Thai Sauce; stir until well combined. Fold in the chopped peanuts and green onions. Weigh the entire recipe and divide the weight by four to get the amount needed to fill one serving.

SALSA VERDE CHICKEN BURRITOS

Makes 4 servings
350 calories / 11F / 34C / 28P / per serving

---

9 oz. grilled chicken breast (12 oz. raw)
1 yellow bell pepper, chopped
3 Tbs. uncooked white, jasmine rice
1 cup Salsa Verde Green Salsa
4 whole grain tortillas (120 calories)
Filling per serving:
2 Tbs. low-fat, shredded mozzarella cheese
½ Tbs. Cashew Sour Cream (recipe in Food Prep Guide)
Topping per serving:
20g avocado
1 cup shredded lettuce
Fresh cilantro

1. Add the raw chicken, bell peppers, uncooked rice and salsa to a crockpot and cook on low for 4-6 hours; shred the chicken. Weigh the mixture and divide the weight by four to get the amount needed to fill one serving.

2. Lay out the tortillas and evenly distribute the chicken mixture and the filling per serving to each one. Roll up tight.

3. Crisp in a panini maker/sauté pan for about ten minutes or until heated through. Garnish the burritos with avocado, lettuce and cilantro.

BEEF & BROCCOLI STIR FRY

Makes 4 servings

345 calories / 11F / 33C / 28P / per serving

16 oz. sirloin tip steak

Veggies:

4 cups chopped broccoli

2 cups chopped sugar snap peas

2 cups water chestnuts

1 cup sliced red onion

Sea salt and pepper, to taste

Teriyaki Marinade:

¼ cup coconut aminos or low-sodium soy sauce

2 Tbs. raw honey

1 Tbs. olive oil

2 tsp. rice vinegar

1 tsp. minced garlic

1. Whisk together all of the marinade ingredients in a bowl.

2. Heat a skillet to medium-high heat. Spray the skillet with cooking spray and add the steak. Cook for two minutes per side. Remove from the pan.

3. Heat the skillet to medium and spray with cooking spray. Add the veggies, marinade, sea salt and pepper. Sauté for about five minutes or until the veggies are tender-crisp. Add the steak to the pan. Cook one minute or until everything is heated through. Weigh the entire recipe and divide the weight by four to get the amount needed to fill one serving.

CRANBERRY, PEAR & TURKEY SALAD

Makes 4 servings
350 calories / 13F / 33C / 25P / per serving

8 cups chopped spinach
12 oz. cooked and chopped turkey breast
2 (300g) chopped pears
1 cup unsweetened dried cranberries
¼ cup shelled pumpkin seeds
1 tsp. chia seeds

Honey Vinaigrette:
2 Tbs. light tasting olive oil
2 Tbs. raw honey
1 Tbs. apple cider vinegar
Dash sea salt
Dash dry mustard
Dash black pepper

1. Place all the ingredients for the Honey Vinaigrette into a blender and blend until smooth. Weigh the dressing and divide the weight by four to get the amount needed to fill one serving.

2. In a bowl, layer two cups of spinach, 3 oz. turkey breast, 75g pears, ¼ cup of cranberries, one tablespoon of pumpkin seeds and ¼ teaspoon of chia seeds for one serving. Drizzle the vinaigrette over the top.

GARDEN VEGGIE PIZZA

Makes 4 servings
335 calories / 12F / 33C / 23P / per serving

¾ cup white whole wheat flour
1 tsp. baking powder
¼ tsp. sea salt
Dash of garlic powder
Dash of onion powder
½ cup plain, nonfat Greek yogurt
¾ cup traditional marinara sauce
2 large chicken sausage links (160 cals each), chopped or sliced
1 cup low-fat, shredded mozzarella cheese
1 tomato, sliced
½ cup sliced red onion
½ cup sliced mushrooms
½ cup canned, chopped, roasted artichoke hearts
½ cup sliced olives
Dash of garlic powder
Dash of oregano
Sea salt and pepper, to taste

1. Preheat the oven to 425 degrees.

2. Whisk the flour, baking powder, sea salt, garlic powder and onion powder together in a bowl. Add the Greek yogurt and use a rubber spatula to fold it in until well combined. If the dough is too dry, add a tiny bit of water; if it's too sticky, flour the surface before rolling out.

3. Roll the dough out into a circle and place on a greased baking sheet or pizza stone. Spray with cooking spray and bake for 6-8 minutes.

4. Evenly spread the marinara sauce over the dough. Layer the chicken sausage, cheese and veggies. Sprinkle garlic powder, oregano, salt and pepper on top of the veggies.

4. Bake on the bottom rack of your oven for 10-15 minutes or until the cheese is melted and the veggies are tender. Slice into four equal servings. Enjoy warm.

THAI PROTEIN BOWL

Makes 4 servings
330 calories / 12F / 32C / 24P / per serving

6 oz. cooked, shredded chicken breast (8 oz. raw)
¾ cup cooked quinoa (¼ cup uncooked)
2 cups chopped broccoli
1 cup sliced bell peppers
Sea salt
8 cups chopped kale
¼ cup Bolthouse Farms Cilantro Avocado Dressing
1 cup chopped cucumbers
2 oz. raw cashews

Thai Peanut Dressing:

1 Tbs. OffBeat Sweet Classic Peanut Butter
   or natural peanut butter
1 Tbs. raw honey
½ Tbs. olive oil
1 tsp. water
1 tsp. rice vinegar
1 tsp. coconut aminos or low-sodium soy sauce
Dash of sea salt
Dash of cayenne pepper

1. Cook the chicken according to the directions in the Food Prep Guide. Cook the quinoa according to the directions on the package.

2. Place the broccoli and bell peppers on a baking sheet lined with parchment paper. Spray the tops with cooking spray and sprinkle with sea salt. Roast in the oven at 375 degrees for 20 minutes.

3. Place all dressing ingredients in a blender and blend until smooth. Weigh the dressing and divide the weight by four to get the amount needed to fill one serving.

4. Chop the kale and massage with the Bolthouse Dressing. Top two cups of kale with three tablespoons of cooked quinoa, ¼ of the shredded chicken, ¼ of the roasted broccoli and peppers, ¼ cup of raw cucumbers and ½ oz. of raw cashews. Drizzle one serving of the Thai Peanut dressing over the top.

GRILLED CAPRESE PANINI

Makes 4 servings
350 calories / 12F / 33C / 26P / per serving

6 oz. cooked chicken breast (8 oz. raw)
1 cup baby kale
5 oz. fresh, sliced mozzarella
4 tomato slices
2 Tbs. balsamic glaze
Fresh basil
2 large pieces Stonefire naan bread (126g each)

1. Cook the chicken according to directions in the Food Prep Guide.

2. Layer the kale, tomato slices, chicken, mozzarella and basil in between both pieces of naan bread. Place in a greased pan or panini press over medium heat. Cook until the cheese is melted and the outside of the naan bread is golden and crispy. Slice into four equal portions, drizzle the balsamic glaze inside and enjoy warm.

SALSA CHICKEN PILE-UP

Makes 4 servings
340 calories / 12F / 32C / 26P / per serving

9 oz. grilled chicken breast (12 oz. raw)
1 cup salsa
½ cup cooked white or brown jasmine rice (3 Tbs. uncooked)
1 cup diced red bell peppers
1 cup diced yellow onions
½ cup black beans, rinsed and drained
4 cups shredded lettuce
4 Tbs. sliced olives
4 oz. guacamole
4 Tbs. Cashew Sour Cream (recipe Food Prep Guide)
Diced jalapeños, for garnish
Green onions, for garnish

1. Place raw chicken and salsa together in a crockpot, cook on low for three hours. Shred and then cook an additional 1-2 hours. Weigh the chicken mixture and divide the weight by four to get the amount needed to fill one serving.

2. Cook the rice according to the directions on the package.

3. Add the red peppers and onions to a greased frying pan over medium heat. Sauté the red peppers until tender; set aside.

4. For one serving, layer: one cup shredded lettuce, two table-spoons of cooked rice, ¼ of the salsa chicken, two tablespoons of black beans, ¼ of the sautéed peppers and onions, one table-spoon of olives, 1 oz. guacamole, one tablespoon of Cashew Sour Cream, jalapeños and green onions. Enjoy!

ROASTED BUTTERNUT SQUASH SOUP

Makes 4 servings
350 calories / 13F / 34C / 24P / per serving

8 oz. raw butternut squash
6 oz. raw sweet potato
1 medium-sized carrot, skinned and chopped
1 celery stick
¼ cup chopped yellow onion
1 Tbs. olive oil
1 cup low-sodium chicken broth
1 cup water
Sea salt and pepper, to taste
1 large piece of Stonefire naan bread (126g)
Toppings per serving:
2 slices turkey bacon, cooked and chopped
2 Tbs. plain, nonfat Greek yogurt
2 Tbs. low-fat, shredded mozzarella cheese
Chives, for garnish

1. Preheat oven to 400 degrees.

2. Chop all the veggies, sweet potatoes and squash. Place in a single layer on a large baking sheet lined with parchment paper. Drizzle with olive oil and sprinkle with sea salt. Roast for 40 minutes, flipping halfway.

3. Remove from the oven and pour all ingredients from the pan into a high-powered blender with water, chicken broth, salt and pepper (or add to a large pot and use a hand emulsifier). If the soup is too thick, add more water until you reach your desired consistency. Weigh the entire soup and divide the weight by four to get the amount needed to fill one serving.

4. Serve warm topped with bacon, yogurt, cheese and chives. Use ¼ of the naan bread per serving for dipping.

MAPLE PECAN GLAZED SALMON

Makes 4 servings
350 calories / 11F / 34C / 28P / per serving

---

12 oz. wild caught salmon
Dash of sea salt
Dash of pepper
Dash of ground ginger
4 slices turkey bacon, chopped
4 Tbs. chopped pecans
2 Tbs. pure maple syrup
Sides per serving:
100g sweet potatoes, cubed and roasted
1 cup broccoli, roasted

1. Roast 400g sweet potatoes and four cups of broccoli according to the directions in the Food Prep Guide.

2. Heat the oven to HI broil. Place the salmon skin side down on a greased baking sheet and lightly season with salt, pepper and ground ginger. Broil for about 15 minutes or until it begins to flake.

3. Grease a small frying pan and heat over medium heat. Place the chopped bacon and pecans in the pan and toast for three minutes. Add the pure maple syrup and heat together for about one minute.

4. Top ¼ of the salmon and ¼ of the sweet potatoes with ¼ of the caramelized bacon and pecans mixture per serving. Enjoy ¼ of the broccoli on the side.

CREAMY CHICKEN CORN CHOWDER

Makes 4 servings
350 calories / 12F / 34C / 26P / per serving

---

4 oz. cooked, shredded chicken breast (5.2 oz. raw)
2 Tbs. grass-fed butter
1 cup diced red bell pepper
½ cup diced yellow onion
1 jalapeño, seeded and finely chopped
2 cloves garlic, minced
2 Tbs. CSE Buttermilk Pancake & Waffle Mix
2 cups low-sodium chicken broth
8 oz. raw red potatoes, diced
2 bay leaves
Sea salt and pepper, to taste
2 cups fresh or frozen corn
½ cup plain, nonfat Greek yogurt

Toppings per serving:
2 Tbs. low-fat, shredded mozzarella cheese
1 slice cooked, chopped turkey bacon
Green onions, chopped

1. Cook chicken and bacon according to the directions in the Food Prep Guide. Cook the bacon according to the directions on the package.

2. In a large pot, melt the butter over medium heat. Add the red bell peppers, onions and jalapeños; sauté until tender, about three minutes. Add the garlic and cook until fragrant. Stir in the CSE Pancake & Waffle Mix and then slowly whisk in the chicken broth until well blended.

3. Add the potatoes, bay leaves, salt and pepper to taste. Bring mixture to a boil, stirring constantly. Reduce heat to medium-low and cook uncovered, about 10 minutes or until the potatoes are tender.

4. Add in the cooked chicken, corn and Greek yogurt. Simmer uncovered for 10-15 minutes, stirring occasionally. Weigh the entire recipe and divide the weight by four to get the amount needed to fill one serving. Serve warm topped with cheese, bacon and green onions.

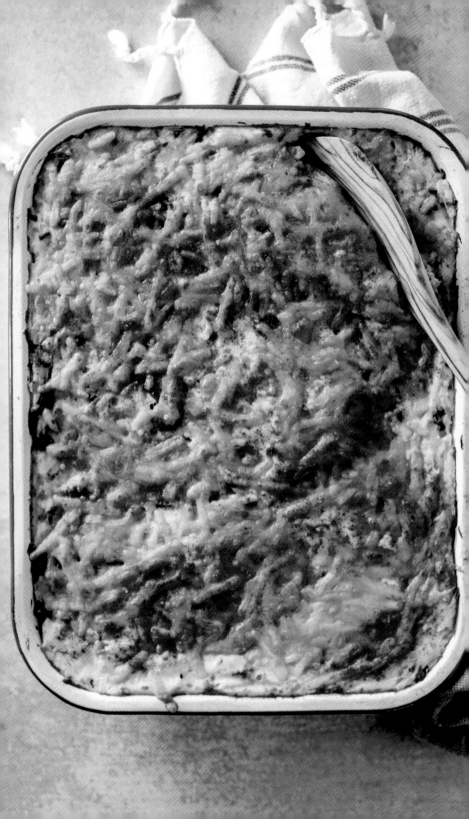

SHEPHERD'S PIE

Makes 4 servings
350 calories / 11F / 35C / 27P / per serving

---

15 oz. peeled red potatoes
½ cup plain, nonfat Greek yogurt
½ cup shredded, sharp cheddar cheese
Dash sea salt
Dash pepper
3 cups green beans, fresh or frozen
½ cup diced yellow onions
1 tsp. minced garlic
12 oz. lean ground turkey
½ cup tomato paste
1 cup vetetable stock
4 tsp. Worcestershire sauce
1 tsp. Stevia in the Raw
Dash paprika

1. Bring a pot of water to a boil. Add the potatoes and boil for 20 minutes. Mash with the Greek yogurt, ½ of the cheese and salt and pepper; set aside.

2. Chop green beans and steam for 20 minutes.

3. Heat a large sauté pan or skillet over medium-high and spray with cooking spray. Sauté the onions and garlic until tender. Add the raw ground turkey. Cook until browned then add salt and pepper to taste. Stir in the green beans, tomato paste, vegetable stock, stevia and Worcestershire sauce. Cover and simmer on medium-low for five minutes.

4. Preheat the oven to 350 degrees.

5. Spray an 8x8 baking dish with cooking spray. Add the meat and green beans to the bottom of the pan, spread the potatoes over the top, then sprinkle with the remaining ¼ cup of cheese and paprika. Bake 10-15 minutes or until the cheese is melted and everything is heated through.

BUTTERNUT SQUASH & SAUSAGE RISOTTO

Makes 4 servings
350 calories / 12F / 35C / 25P / per serving

½ cup + 2 Tbs. uncooked white or brown jasmine rice
   (1 ¾ cup cooked)
1 ½ cups vegetable stock
2 cups raw butternut squash
10 oz. raw lean ground turkey
1 shallot, sliced
½ clove garlic, minced
2 Italian chicken sausage links (160 cals each)
2 cups chopped spinach
Toppings per serving:
Sea salt and black pepper, to taste
1 Tbs. grated Parmesan cheese
Cilantro, for garnish

1. Cook the rice according to the directions on the package, using vegetable stock for the liquid.

2. Preheat the oven to 400 degrees. Peel and cube the butternut squash. Place on a baking sheet lined with parchment paper. Spray the tops with cooking spray and sprinkle with sea salt and pepper. Roast in the oven for 30 minutes, flipping halfway. Set aside.

3. In a large skillet or pan, brown the ground turkey over medium heat. Once browned, add the shallots and garlic, sliced chicken sausage and chopped spinach. Cook until the garlic is fragrant, sausage is browned and spinach is wilted. Turn heat down to low.

4. Add the cooked rice and roasted butternut squash to the skillet and stir until well combined. Weigh the entire recipe and divide the weight by four to find the amount needed to fill one serving. Top each serving with salt, pepper, Parmesan cheese and cilantro.

BBQ CHICKEN AVOCADO WRAP

Makes 4 servings
330 calories / 10F / 33C / 28P / per serving

8 oz. cooked chicken breast (10.6 oz. raw)
½ cup Stubb's Original BBQ Sauce
½ cup thin sliced red onions
2 cups chopped butter lettuce
8 tomato slices
200g chopped avocado
4 Flatout wraps or Joseph's flatbread wraps (100 cals each)

1. Cook and shred the chicken according to the directions in the Food Prep Guide.

2. Combine the chicken and the BBQ sauce in a bowl. Weigh the mixture and divide by four to get the amount needed for one serving.

3. Lay out the wraps and layer ¼ of the BBQ chicken, onions, lettuce, tomato slices and 50g avocado inside each one. Roll up tight and enjoy cold.

CAPRESE PASTA BOWL

Makes 4 servings
345 calories / 11F / 35C / 26P / per serving

---

5 oz. dry brown rice penne pasta (2 ¾ cup cooked)
2 cups chopped broccoli
7.5 oz. cooked chicken breast (10 oz. raw)
1 tsp. minced garlic
Salt and pepper, to taste
1 cup cherry tomatoes, halved
2 cups chopped spinach
1 Tbs. avocado or olive oil
4 oz. fresh mozzarella pearls
Handful of fresh, chopped basil

Topping:
Drizzle of balsamic glaze

1. Preheat the oven to 400 degrees. Cook pasta according to the directions on the package. Roast the broccoli according to the instructions in the Food Prep Guide.

2. Chop the raw chicken. Heat a skillet over medium heat. Spray with cooking spray and add the chicken, garlic, salt and pepper. Sauté until the chicken is cooked through; remove from pan.

3. Halve the tomatoes. Chop the roasted broccoli and spinach. Heat oil in the skillet and then add all the veggies with a little salt and pepper. Sauté for three minutes. Add the cooked chicken, cooked pasta, fresh mozzarella pearls and basil to the pan. Stir until everything is well combined.

4. Weigh the entire recipe and divide the weight by four to get the amount needed to fill one serving. Enjoy warm or cold with a drizzle of balsamic glaze.

THAI CHICKEN SOUP

Makes 4 servings
345 calories / 10F / 35C / 28P / per serving

---

1 Tbs. red curry paste
1 ½ cups light coconut milk, canned
1 cup low-sodium chicken stock
1 Tbs. fish sauce
1 Tbs. raw honey
2 Tbs. OffBeat Sweet Classic Peanut Butter
  or natural peanut butter
14 oz. raw chicken breast (10.5 oz. cooked, sliced chicken breast)
1 cup sliced red bell pepper
½ cup thin sliced yellow onion
1 cup peeled, chopped carrots
2 tsp. fresh, grated ginger
½ cup uncooked white or brown jasmine rice

Toppings per serving:
Lime wedge
Cilantro, for garnish

1. In a crockpot, whisk together the curry paste, coconut milk, chicken stock, fish sauce, honey and peanut butter. Cut the chicken into slices. Add in the chicken, uncooked rice, red bell peppers, onions, carrots and ginger. Cover and cook on low for six hours or on high for four hours.

2. Weigh the entire soup and divide by four to get the amount needed to fill one serving. Spoon into bowls. Top each serving with lime juice and cilantro. Enjoy warm.

MAPLE DIJON PROTEIN BOWL

Makes 4 servings
350 calories / 12F / 36C / 24P / per serving

---

2 cups cooked quinoa (1 cup uncooked)
8 oz. yellow pepper, thinly sliced
4 oz. red onion, thinly sliced
12 oz. sirloin tip steak
4 cups mixed salad greens
Maple Dijon Vinaigrette:
2 Tbs. plain, nonfat Greek yogurt
2 Tbs. Balsamic vinegar
2 Tbs. pure maple syrup
1 Tbs. avocado oil or light tasting olive oil
2 tsp. Dijon mustard
½ tsp. minced garlic
Dash of black pepper

1. Cook the quinoa according to the directions on the package. Heat the oven to 400 degrees.

2. Place the peppers and onions on a baking sheet. Spray the tops with cooking spray and sprinkle with sea salt. Roast 10-15 minutes.

3. Slice steak thin. Heat a skillet to medium heat and spray with cooking spray. Place the steak in a skillet and cook until you reach the desired doneness.

4. Place all the dressing ingredients into a blender. Blend until smooth. Weigh the dressing and divide the weight by four to get the amount needed to fill one serving.

5. For one serving, layer one cup mixed greens, ½ cup of cooked quinoa, ¼ of the steak, ¼ of the roasted bell peppers and onions. Drizzle one serving of the dressing over the top. Sprinkle with sea salt and pepper to taste.

CHEDDAR RANCH CHICKEN & POTATOES

Makes 4 servings
340 calories / 11F / 34C / 26P / per serving

4 cups raw broccoli
20 oz. baby gold potatoes
Sea salt and pepper, to taste
1 Tbs. grass-fed butter
1 Tbs. CSE Buttermilk Pancake & Waffle Mix
1 cup unsweetened almond milk
2 tsp. ranch DIPS powder
6 oz. cooked, shredded chicken breast (8 oz. raw)
1 cup low-fat, shredded cheddar cheese
Toppings per serving:
1 Tbs. plain, nonfat Greek yogurt
Green onions, for garnish

1. Preheat the oven to 400 degrees. Chop the broccoli and place on a baking sheet lined with parchment paper. Spray the tops with cooking spray and sprinkle with sea salt. Roast in the oven for 20 minutes. Remove from the oven and let cool.

2. Bring a large pot of water to a boil. Add the potatoes and sea salt, then boil for 15-20 minutes or until fork-tender; drain. Smash lightly and set aside.

3. Place the pot back on the stove over medium heat and add the butter. Stir until melted, then stir in the CSE Pancake & Waffle Mix. Once combined, add in the milk, ranch powder and a dash of salt and pepper. Bring to a boil then let simmer on medium for 5 minutes. Fold in the shredded chicken, roasted broccoli, smashed potatoes and ½ cup of the cheese.

4. Transfer to a greased 8x8 baking dish and top with the remaining cheese. Bake for 10-15 minutes or until the cheese is melted. Divide the casserole into four equal servings and top each serving with one tablespoon of Greek yogurt and sliced green onions. Enjoy!

TOMATO BASIL SPAGHETTI & MEATBALLS

Makes 4 servings

345 calories / 12F / 34C / 25P / per serving

---

6 cups roasted spaghetti squash
3 slices Sprouted Grain Ezekiel Bread
2 Tbs. unsweetened almond milk
2 egg whites (¼ cup liquid egg whites)
12 oz. raw lean ground turkey
¼ cup grated Parmesan cheese
¼ tsp. sea salt
Dash of black pepper
Dash of garlic powder
Tomato Basil Sauce:
1 Tbs. grass-fed butter or olive oil
¼ cup minced yellow onions
1 tsp. minced garlic
28 oz. diced tomatoes, fresh or canned
¼ tsp. dried oregano
½ tsp. sea salt
1 tsp. raw honey
1 Tbs. arrowroot starch or corn starch
2 Tbs. fresh, chopped basil

1. Roast the spaghetti squash and make bread crumbs according to directions in the Food Prep Guide.

2. Whisk the milk and egg whites together. Add the raw turkey, cheese, salt, pepper, garlic powder and bread crumbs. Mix together with hands until well combined. Form into rounded tablespoon-sized balls and place on a greased baking sheet. Broil on high for 3-4 minutes.

3. Make sauce by melting the butter in a sauce pan over medium heat. Sauté the onions and garlic until tender and fragrant. Purée the tomatoes in a blender. Add the puréed tomatoes to the pot; stir until well combined. Stir in the remaining ingredients and bring to a boil. Turn heat down to low.

4. Place the meatballs and sauce in a slow cooker or crockpot. Cook on low for 4 hours. Serve ¼ of the meatballs and sauce over 1 ½ cups of roasted spaghetti squash for one serving. Enjoy warm.

FALL MAPLE HASH

Makes 4 servings
345 calories / 13F / 33C / 24P / per serving

4 cups raw acorn squash
18 small Sugarhouse Maple Chicken Sausage Links
¼ cup slivered almonds
1 cup chopped yellow onion
4 cups thin sliced Brussels sprouts
Salt and pepper, to taste
1 Tbs. pure maple syrup

1. Bring a pot of water to a boil. Cube and peel the acorn squash. Add the squash to the boiling water and boil for 4-5 minutes. Drain and set aside.

2. Spray a large skillet with cooking spray and heat to medium-high heat. Slice the chicken sausage into rounds and throw into the skillet with the almonds. Cook for five minutes. Remove from the pan and set aside.

3. Spray the skillet again, then add the onions and sliced Brussels sprouts. Sauté for three minutes. Add the acorn squash, sausage, almonds and pure maple syrup. Cook for another three minutes. Season with salt and pepper. Weigh the entire recipe and divide by four to get the amount needed to fill one serving. Enjoy warm.

SLOPPY SWEET POTATO

Makes 4 servings
345 calories / 10.5F / 35C / 27.5P / per serving

---

14 oz. raw gold or white sweet potatoes
16 oz. raw, lean ground turkey
1 cup chopped yellow onion
½ cup canned, crushed tomatoes
2 tsp. ground cumin
1 tsp. chili powder
½ tsp. minced garlic
1 Tbs. raw honey
1 Tbs. Worcestershire sauce
2 tsp. apple cider vinegar
Sea salt and pepper, to taste
Toppings per serving:
1 Tbs. chopped green onions
1 Tbs. low-fat, shredded cheddar cheese
Side per serving:
1 cup roasted broccoli

1. Preheat the oven to 425 degrees. Poke holes in the sweet potatoes with a fork and place on a baking sheet lined with parchment paper. Spray the tops with cooking spray and sprinkle with sea salt. Bake for 45-60 minutes, flipping halfway.

2. While the sweet potatoes are baking, heat a large pan or skillet over medium heat. Add the ground turkey and onions; cook until the turkey is browned. Add the crushed tomatoes, cumin, chili powder, garlic, honey, Worcestershire sauce, apple cider vinegar and salt and pepper. Simmer for 20 minutes.

3. Weigh the turkey mixture and sweet potatoes separately. Divide the weight by four to get the amount needed to fill one serving. Place one serving of the turkey on one serving of the sweet potatoes, then top with cheese and green onions. Enjoy the roasted broccoli on the side.

MEDITERRANEAN BOUNTY BOWL

Makes 4 servings
340 calories / 10.5F / 33C / 28.5P / per serving

---

10 oz. cooked chicken breast (13.3 oz. raw)
½ cup cooked quinoa (¼ cup uncooked)
4 cups spinach
2 cups sliced cucumbers
12 mini bell peppers, sliced
20 cherry tomatoes, halved
20 Kalamata olives, pitted
4 Tbs. hummus
120g Bolthouse Farms Italian Vinaigrette Dressing

1. Cook the chicken according to the directions in the Food Prep Guide. Cook the quinoa according to the instructions on the package.

2. Add to a bowl for one serving: 1 cup spinach, ½ cup chopped cucumbers, three sliced mini bell peppers, five cherry tomatoes, five Kalamata olives, 2.5 ounces cooked chicken and two tablespoons of cooked quinoa. Top with one tablespoon of hummus and then drizzle 30g dressing over the top.

CHEESY ROASTED VEGGIES & SAUSAGE

Makes 4 servings
350 calories / 13F / 33C / 26P / per serving

---

24 oz. raw butternut squash
6 large chicken sausage links (160 cals each)
4 cups fresh or frozen green beans
4 garlic and herb Laughing Cow Cheese wedges
Sea salt and pepper, to taste

1. Preheat the oven to 400 degrees.

2. Peel and cube the butternut squash. Slice the chicken sausage into rounds.

3. Place the squash, green beans and sausage on a baking sheet lined with parchment paper. Spray the tops with cooking spray and sprinkle with sea salt and pepper. Roast in the oven for 20 minutes. Flip and add the cheese wedges to the pan. Roast for another 10 minutes.

4. Dump the entire sheet pan into a large bowl and stir until the cheese is melted over all the veggies and sausage. Weigh the entire recipe and divide by four to get the amount needed to fill one serving. Enjoy warm.

WHITE CHICKEN CHILI

Makes 4 servings
340 calories / 10.5F / 33C / 28P / per serving

½ cup chopped yellow onions
½ of a jalapeño, seeded and minced
1 tsp. minced garlic
1 cup great northern white beans
1 ½ cups low-sodium chicken stock
4 oz. canned, diced green chiles
½ cup frozen yellow corn
2 tsp. cumin
1 tsp. coriander
½ tsp. chili powder
Pinch of sea salt
Dash of black pepper
4 corn tortillas (6 inch)

Toppings per serving:
2.5 oz. rotisserie chicken breast, shredded
2 Tbs. plain, nonfat Greek yogurt
50g avocado
Cilantro, for garnish
Lime wedge, for garnish

1. Spray a large saucepan with cooking spray. Add the onions, jalapeños, and garlic. Sauté until fragrant. Add the beans, chicken stock, chiles, corn and seasonings. Bring to a boil. Reduce the heat and simmer for 30 minutes.

2. Preheat the oven to 400 degrees. Make homemade tortilla strips by slicing the tortillas into thin strips with a pizza cutter. Place on a baking sheet lined with parchment paper. Spray the tops with cooking spray and sprinkle with sea salt and chili powder. Bake for 8-10 minutes or until crispy. Set aside.

3. Remove soup from the heat. Weigh the entire soup and divide by four to get the amount needed to fill one serving. Pour evenly into bowls. Garnish each soup with shredded chicken, Greek yogurt, avocado, cilantro and lime.

BLTA WAFFLE SANDWICH

Makes 4 servings

350 calories / 12F / 35C / 26P / per serving

1 ¾ cups CSE Buttermilk Pancake & Waffle Mix
1 ½ cups water
¼ cup low-fat, shredded cheddar cheese
¼ cup sliced green onions
8 slices turkey bacon
Green leaf lettuce
4 tomato slices
80g avocado slices
Honey Mustard Sauce:
1 Tbs. olive oil mayo
1 Tbs. Dijon mustard
1 tsp. yellow mustard
1 Tbs. raw honey
1 tsp. white wine vinegar
Dash paprika
Dash sea salt
Dash black pepper

1. Whisk all of the Honey Mustard Sauce ingredients together until well combined. Weigh the sauce and divide by four to get the amount needed for one serving. Cover and store in the fridge.

2. Heat a waffle maker. Make waffles by mixing the CSE Pancake & Waffle Mix, water, shredded cheese and green onions together in a bowl. If the batter is too thick, add more water, one tablespoon at a time. Pour the batter onto the greased waffle maker and cook until golden brown. Divide the waffles into four servings and use as a bun.

3. Cook the bacon until crispy.

4. For one serving, sandwich two slices of cooked bacon, lettuce, one tomato slice and 20g avocado in between one serving of the waffle buns. Sprinkle sea salt and pepper on top of the veggies. Use the Honey Mustard Sauce as a dip for the sandwiches. Enjoy warm.

STACKED CHICKEN ENCHILADAS
Makes 4 serving
350 calories / 10.5F / 33.4C / 26P / per serving

---

8 oz. cooked, shredded chicken breasts (10.6 oz. raw)
½ cup minced yellow onion
½ cup minced red bell pepper
½ cup kidney or black beans
½ cup frozen yellow corn
1 cup finely chopped spinach
1 Tbs. taco seasoning
6 corn tortillas (6 inch)
1 ½ cups red or green enchilada sauce
½ cup low-fat, shredded mozzarella cheese
Toppings per serving:
1 Tbs. plain, nonfat Greek yogurt
1 Tbs. pico de gallo or salsa
30g sliced avocado or guacamole
Green onions

1. Cook the chicken according to the directions in the Food Prep Guide. Heat the oven to 375 degrees.

2. Spray a skillet or frying pan with cooking spray and add minced onions and bell peppers. Cook on medium-high heat until tender. Add the chicken, beans, thawed corn, chopped spinach and taco seasoning to the pan. Stir together until heated through and well combined.

3. Spray a square baking dish with cooking spray and layer ½ cup enchilada sauce, three corn tortillas, ½ of the chicken mixture, ¼ cup of cheese, ½ cup enchilada sauce, three corn tortillas, ½ of the chicken mixture, ½ cup enchilada sauce and ¼ cup of cheese. Place in the oven and bake for 20 minutes.

4. Slice into four servings and top each serving with Greek yogurt, Pico De Gallo, fresh avocado slices and green onions.

PESTO CHICKEN SLIDERS
Makes 4 servings
350 calories / 12F / 33C / 27P / per serving

---

18 oz. raw sweet potatoes
10 oz. cooked, shredded chicken breast (13.3 oz. raw)
4 Tbs. pesto sauce
4 cups broccolini
1 Tbs. olive oil
Sea salt, to taste

1. Cook chicken according to the directions in the Food Prep Guide.

2. Heat the oven to 400 degrees. Slice the sweet potatoes into 16 rounds. Place on a baking sheet lined with parchment paper. Spray the tops with cooking spray and sprinkle with sea salt. Bake for 20 minutes. Flip and bake for an additional 20 minutes.

3. Add the broccolini to a baking sheet lined with parchment paper. Drizzle olive oil over the top and sprinkle with sea salt. Bake at 400 degrees for 20 minutes.

4. Add the pesto sauce to the shredded chicken. Weigh the mixture and divide the weight by four to get the amount needed to fill one serving. Sandwich the pesto chicken evenly between the sweet potato rounds. Two sliders per serving. Enjoy the roasted broccolini on the side.

PHILLY CHEESESTEAK WRAPS

Makes 4 servings
350 calories / 14F / 26C / 30P / per serving

---

1 red bell pepper, sliced
1 yellow onion, sliced into rings
5 oz. raw ribeye steak, sliced thin into strips
6 oz. raw chicken breasts, sliced thin strips
1 green bell pepper, sliced
1 Tbs. Italian seasoning
Sea salt, to taste
Ground black pepper, to taste
4 Joseph Flatbread Wraps
½ cup shredded provolone cheese
Side per serving:
¼ cup raspberries

1. Spray a large skillet with cooking spray. Add the bell peppers and onions to the skillet and sprinkle with sea salt. Cover and sauté over medium-high heat for 5-10 minutes or until softened. Place on a plate and set aside.

2. Add steak and chicken to the skillet. Cook and break up into small pieces until completely cooked through and no longer pink. Turn heat to low and add the onions and peppers back to the pan. Toss together and season with Italian seasoning, salt and pepper. Weigh the mixture and divide the weight by four to get the amount needed to fill one serving.

3. Preheat the oven to 350 degrees.

4. Spread one serving of the mixture over each flatbread. Sprinkle two tablespoons of provolone cheese over each one and roll up tight. Place wraps on a baking sheet and heat in the oven for 5-10 minutes or until the bread is warm and the cheese is melted. One wrap per serving. Enjoy ¼ cup of raspberries on the side.

BUFFALO CHICKEN & MOZZARELLA MEATBALLS

Makes 4 servings
350 calories / 10F / 34C / 28P / per serving

---

14 oz. raw red potatoes, cut into wedges
12 oz. raw ground chicken breast
¼ cup Panko breadcrumbs
1 large egg
2 Tbs. sliced green onions
1 tsp. minced garlic
½ tsp. sea salt
¼ cup Frank's hot sauce, divided
2 regular string cheese sticks
4 Tbs. Bolthouse Farms Chunky Bleu Cheese or
   Bolthouse Farms Classic Ranch Dressing
8 celery sticks
8 oz. carrots sticks
Topping per serving:
7g bleu or feta cheese crumbles on top

1. Heat oven to 400 degrees. Slice potatoes into fries or wedges and place on a baking sheet lined with parchment paper. Spray the tops with cooking spray and season with sea salt and other seasonings of choice. Bake for 40-50 minutes, flipping halfway. Weigh the potatoes once cooked and divide the weight by four to get the amount needed for one serving.

2. Add the chicken, breadcrumbs, egg, green onion, garlic, sea salt and one tablespoon of the hot sauce to a large bowl. Mix with hands until well combined. Slice each string cheese stick into six pieces. Shape the chicken into balls using two tablespoons of turkey per ball. Place one piece of cheese in the middle of each one. Should make 12 meatballs. Add meatballs to a greased square glass baking dish.

3. Place the meatballs in the oven at 400 degrees for 18-20 minutes. Place the meatballs in a bowl once cooked and toss with the remaining hot sauce.

4. Enjoy each serving of meatballs and potatoes with two celery sticks and two ounces of carrots. Drizzle one tablespoon of the dressing over the top of everything and sprinkle with cheese crumbles.

CHINESE SESAME CHICKEN
Makes 4 servings
350 calories / 12F / 33C / 27P / per serving

¾ cup cooked white or brown jasmine rice (¼ cup uncooked)
16 oz. raw cauliflower rice
15 oz. raw ground (or diced) chicken breast
½ tsp. sea salt
1 tsp. minced garlic
1 Tbs. fresh, grated ginger
2 tsp. chili paste or Sriracha sauce
¼ cup coconut palm sugar
¼ cup coconut aminos or low-sodium soy sauce
2 Tbs. sesame oil
½ cup low-sodium chicken broth
1 Tbs. arrowroot or cornstarch (sauce thickener)
Green onions, sliced for garnish
4 tsp. sesame seeds

1. Cook the rice and cauliflower rice according to the directions on the package. Keep warm.

2. Heat a skillet over medium-high heat. Spray with cooking spray and add the chicken. Break up and cook until no longer pink. Turn heat to medium and add sea salt, garlic and fresh ginger. Cook for one minute. Stir in the chili paste or Sriracha sauce and the coconut sugar.

3. Whisk together the coconut aminos, sesame oil, chicken broth and cornstarch or arrowroot powder in a bowl. Pour over chicken and bring to a simmer. Continue to stir for 3-5 minutes until the sauce begins to thicken. If the sauce gets too thick, add in more chicken stock a little at a time.

4. Weigh the chicken mixture and divide by four to get the amount needed for one serving. Serve the chicken warm over 4 oz. cauliflower rice and three tablespoons of cooked rice. Top with green onions and one teaspoon of sesame seeds.

DAILY

WORKOUTS

YOU DON'T GET WHAT YOU WISH FOR. YOU GET WHAT YOU WORK FOR.

HIIT

Set your timer for 30 seconds of work, 15 seconds of rest, 8 cycles. Perform each of the following sets 2 times through. For example… Round 1: Complete 30 seconds of T - PUSH-UPS followed by 15 seconds of rest. Now, move to 30 seconds of REVERSE LUNGES followed by 15 seconds of rest. Complete the last two movements and start immediately back at PUSH-UPS for 1 more cycle of each! Rest 90 seconds between rounds.

WARM-UP
5 minutes of brisk walking, jogging in place, jumping rope, etc.

ROUND 1	ROUND 2	ROUND 3
T - PUSH-UPS	PLANK PRESS	COMMANDOS
CURTSY LUNGES	SUMO SQUAT JUMP	PLIÉ SQUAT RAISE
PLANK SHOULDER TAPS	PLANK JACKS	TEMPO MT. CLIMBERS
ALTERNATING SIDE LUNGE	HIGH KNEES	SQUAT JUMPS

ADVANCED WOD
"POWER LADDER"
12-11-10-9-8-7-6-5-4-3-2-1
DEADLIFT
PULL-UPS
DUMBBELL BENCH PRESS

FIND A DEMO VIDEO OF THIS WORKOUT AND ALL WORKOUTS IN OUR CSE+ APP!

TABATA

Set your timer for 20 seconds of work, 10 seconds of rest, 8 cycles. Perform each of the following paired movements 1 time through. For example... Movement 1: Complete 20 seconds of Dumbbell Clean & Press followed by 10 seconds of rest. Now, move to Single Leg V-ups for 20 seconds. Rest 10 seconds and you're moving on to movement #3. Repeat this pattern through the 8 movements. Push as hard as you can for 20 seconds through each interval. Rest 90 seconds between rounds. Complete 4 cycles of the 8 exercises as outlined. Each round will take you 4 minutes.

1. DUMBBELL CLEAN & PRESS
2. SINGLE LEG V-UP
3. DUMBBELL THRUSTERS
4. PLANK

5. DUMBBELL ALT. SNATCH
6. WEIGHTED CRUNCH
7. DUMBBELL JACKS
8. MT. CLIMBERS

ADVANCED WOD

AMRAP'N IT

IN 7 MINUTES, COMPLETE AS MANY ROUNDS + REPS OF THE PAIRED MOVEMENTS IN A GIVEN SET. REST 2 MINUTES BEFORE MOVING ON TO THE NEXT SET.

SET 1 10 DUMBBELL GET-UP SIT-UPS/EACH SIDE
20 DUMBBELL FRONT RACK REVERSE LUNGES

SET 2 10 DUMBBELL FLOOR CHEST PRESS
10 DUMBBELL RENEGADE ROW/EACH SIDE

SET 3 20 SPLIT STANCE ALTERNATING HAMMER CURL
20 SPLIT STANCE ALTERNATING SHOULDER PRESS

STRENGTH

Don't focus on flying through this one! Focus on form and function. Get in tune with your body and dial in on the muscle groups being used. Pay attention to how the body works together as a WHOLE! If this is too easy… add reps. If it's too hard… adjust accordingly. It's all about progression. One day at a time! Grab a bench or a chair for this STRENGTH workout!

COMPLETE 10 REPS + 3 ROUNDS OF THE FOLLOWING:

1. DIPS
2. BENCH HOPS
3. PUSH-UPS
4. SQUAT JUMPS
5. TRICEP PRESS
6. BLASTERS
7. STEP UPS
8. BICYCLES
9. BULGARIAN SPLIT SQUATS
10. JUMP IN N' OUTS
11. SPIDERMAN PLANKS
12. BENCH HOP OVERS

ADVANCED WOD

"O₂ DEFICIT"

START A 25 MINUTE RUNNING CLOCK.
COMPLETE THE REQUIRED REP SCHEMES
IN EACH OF FIVE 5 MINUTE SEGMENTS.

0-5 MINUTES
3 ROUNDS
5 DEADLIFTS
5 PULL-UPS

5-10 MINUTES
21-15-9 (REPS)
DEADLIFTS
V-UPS

10-15 MINUTES
3 ROUNDS
20 KB SNATCHES
30 MT. CLIMBERS

15-20 MINUTES
21-15-9 (REPS)
WALL BALLS
KB SWINGS

20-25 MINUTES
3 ROUNDS
10 THRUSTERS
10 TOES TO BAR

HIIT

Set your timer for 30 seconds of work, 15 seconds of rest, 6 cycles. Perform each of the following movements at 90%+ effort for 30 seconds followed by a short 15 second break. During the 15 seconds of rest gear up for the next movement on the list! Complete 30 seconds of each and then rest 90 seconds between rounds.

WARM-UP
5 minutes of brisk walking, jogging in place, jumping rope, etc.

COMPLETE HIIT CYCLE 3-4X
1. JUMPING JACKS
2. DIVE BOMBER PUSH-UPS
3. SPEED SKATERS
4. STRAIGHT LEG SIT-UPS
5. POWER LUNGES
6. KICK THROUGH BURPEES

ADVANCED WOD
"TRIPLE THREAT"

EACH ROUND IS A 7 MINUTE AMRAP. IN 7 MINUTES, COMPLETE AS MANY ROUNDS + REPS AS POSSIBLE WHILE KEEPING PROPER FORM. REST 2 MINUTES BETWEEN ROUNDS.

ROUND 1	ROUND 2	ROUND 3
5 PULL-UPS	5 HANG CLEANS	5 DEADLIFTS
10 PUSH-UPS	10 TOES TO BAR	10 KB SWINGS
15 AIR SQUATS	30 DOUBLE UNDERS	15 SIT-UPS

STRENGTH

Did you know that BUILDING MUSCLE is the quickest and most efficient way to burn fat? Fact. Time to sculpt those arms and legs! Complete the rep count for each bodyweight movement. Remember, this is a slower day so focus on form. Get in tune with those muscles of yours. If you feel like you have more in the tank after a 3rd round, do additional reps of each or add some weight. Get strong!

WARM-UP

5 minutes of brisk walking, jogging in place, jumping rope, etc.

20 - MT. CLIMBERS
15 - AIR SQUATS
10 - PUSH-UPS
 5 - PIKED SHOULDER PRESSES
10 - BENCH/CHAIR DIPS
15 - SUMO SQUATS
20 - CRUNCHES

REPEAT 3X

ADVANCED WOD
"THE CONDITIONER"

SET 1	SET 2	SET 3
3 ROUNDS FOR TIME	3 ROUNDS FOR TIME	3 ROUNDS FOR TIME
7 POWER CLEANS	7 PULL-UPS	7 BURPEES
2 MINUTE MAX	2 MINUTE MAX	2 MINUTE MAX
CALORIE ROW	DOUBLE UNDERS	PUSH-UPS

SPRINTS

Find a local track, a park or, if you have access to one, a treadmill will be best for this one. Sprints are a great way to boost your metabolism (along with all the other workouts you've done this week!). High intensity interval training has been proven to be one of the most effective fat burning methods ever! There are so many different ways to mix it up! Fitness is supposed to be fun! And as you can see from this week of workouts, you don't need a lot of time or expensive equipment… all you need is YOU!

WARM-UP
5 minutes of brisk walking, jogging in place, jumping rope, etc.

SPRINTS
Perform the following sprint sequence three times through. Rest longer if needed but give these sprints everything you've got! Make sure you are nice and warm before getting after this one!

100 METER SPRINT
REST 30 SECONDS
200 METER SPRINT
REST 45 SECONDS
400 METER SPRINT
REST 2 MINUTES
REPEAT 3X

THE ULTIMATE CLEAN SIMPLE EATS SWAPS AND SUBSTITUTIONS LIST

If you have dietary restrictions or food allergies, you can still use our Clean Simple Eats Meal Plans with these swaps! If you can't find these swaps in store, check online. Amazon and Thrive Market have great options. Keep in mind when making ingredient swaps, the macros for the recipe will change. If you'd like to track your macros accurately, we recommend inputting each recipe into our CSE+ App with individual ingredients.

GENERAL SWAPS:

Avocado: for savory entrees: nuts, cheese, seeds. For sweet recipes such as shakes: canned, full-fat coconut milk, unsweetened coconut flakes or nut butter

Banana: other fruit of choice // example: 50g banana = 140g strawberries, 170g raspberries, 80g blueberries, 80g apples, 115g peaches, 85g pineapple, 75g pears

Bison: lean ground beef

Eggs: for baking: Bob's Red Mill Egg Replacer or replace one egg with three tablespoons water + one tablespoons ground flaxseed or three tablespoons water + one tablespoon ground chia seeds or ¼ cup unsweetened applesauce or ½ of a mashed avocado or ½ of a mashed banana or ¼ cup coconut yogurt. For savory breakfast dishes or entrees (use where applicable): diced chicken, deli turkey, turkey bacon or Follow Your Heart brand Vegan Egg

Ezekiel Bread: Dave's Killer Bread Thin Sliced, Harper's Bran Bread, or any 80 calorie per slice whole grain bread

Fish: chicken breast

Ground Turkey: lean ground chicken or lean ground beef

Honey: pure maple syrup

Oats: cream of wheat, farro

Salmon: cod, halibut, mahi mahi or chicken breast

DAIRY:

Butter: coconut oil

Bolthouse Dressing: Daiya dressings, Primal Kitchen or Tessemae's (use half the amount in all brands)

Cheddar Cheese: Daiya brand or Follow Your Heart brand dairy-free cheddar

Chocolate Chips: Enjoy Life or Nestle Simply Delicious chocolate chips

Cottage Cheese: dairy-free yogurt (see Greek yogurt)

Cream Cheese: Daiya brand dairy-free cream cheese

Feta: Treeline brand cashew cheese

Greek Yogurt: Daiya brand, Silk brand or Kite Hill brand dairy-free plain yogurt

CSE Pancake & Waffle Mix: Annie's Pancake & Waffle Mix, Enjoy Life Pancake & Waffle Mix, or Birch Benders

Laughing Cow Cheese: Daiya brand dairy-free cream cheese or Treeline brand dairy-free soft cheeses

Mayo: Primal Kitchen Mayo, Hellman's Vegan Mayo, Just Mayo, Thrive Market Coconut Oil Mayo, Kraft Olive or Avocado Oil Mayo or make at home

Milk: unsweetened almond milk or cashew milk

Mexican Shredded Cheese: Daiya brand or Follow Your Heart brand dairy-free cheddar

Mozzarella Cheese: Daiya brand dairy-free mozzarella

Parmesan Cheese: Follow Your Heart brand dairy-free shredded Parmesan style cheese

Pepper Jack Cheese: Daiya brand or Follow Your Heart brand dairy-free pepper jack style cheese

Pesto: Vegan, dairy-free basil pesto or make at home

Protein Powder: CSE Vegan Protein Powder (CSE powders are third-party tested lactose-free)

Ricotta Cheese: Kite Hill dairy-free ricotta

NUTS:

Almond butter: any other nut butter, sunbutter or coconut butter

Almonds: any other nuts

Almond extract: vanilla extract

Almond Milk: cashew milk, coconut milk, hemp milk or skim milk

Cashew Sour Cream: plain Greek yogurt

Cashews: any other nut or seed

Coconut: sunflower seeds, any other nut, any other nut butter, sunbutter

Coconut extract: vanilla extract

Coconut Milk (canned): heavy cream for full-fat, Half and Half for light

CSE Pancake & Waffle Mix: Annie's Pancake & Waffle Mix, Enjoy Life Pancake & Waffle Mix

Peanuts: any other nut or seed

Peanut Butter: any other nut butter, sunbutter or coconut butter

Tree-nuts: sunflower seeds, pumpkin seeds, sunbutter, peanuts, peanut butter, coconut, coconut butter

*In savory dishes, any healthy fat may be swapped in for the nuts, i.e. avocado, cheeses, seeds, olives

GLUTEN:

Breadcrumbs: gluten-free breadcrumbs

Buns/Bread: gluten-free bread/buns

CSE Pancake & Waffle Mix: gluten-free Kodiak Cakes Mix, Flap-Jacked Mix or any other gluten-free pancake mix

Oats: gluten-free rolled oats

Pasta: brown rice pasta

Tortillas: corn or brown rice tortillas

Whole Wheat Flour: All-Purpose gluten-free flour

WWW.CLEANSIMPLEEATS.COM